MICHELIN
GUIDE

NORDIC COUNTRIES

DENMARK I FINLAND I ICELAND
NORWAY I SWEDEN

DEAR READER,

We are delighted to introduce the fourth edition of the Michelin guide to the Nordic Countries – a guide to the best places to eat and stay in Denmark, Finland, Iceland, Norway and Sweden. Alongside restaurants and hotels in the main cities, we are also pleased to recommend a selection of our favourite places from smaller towns and villages.

The guide caters for every type of visitor, from business traveller to holiday maker, and highlights the best establishments, from cosy bistros and intimate townhouses to celebrated restaurants and luxury hotels.

The Michelin inspectors are the eyes and ears of our readers and their anonymity is key to ensuring that they receive the same treatment as any other guest. Each year, they search for new establishments to add to the guide, and only the best make it through. Once the annual selection has been made, the 'best of the best' are then recognised with awards: Stars ❀ and Bib Gourmands ☺.

Regular readers will notice that the guide has a different look this year. The most significant change is that the restaurants – our readers' favourite part – now appear at the front of each locality, with the hotels following afterwards. Restaurants are now also ordered according to the quality of their food rather than the comfort of the establishment, with the awards that you already know and love (Michelin Stars and Bib Gourmands) being placed at the top. The remainder of the restaurants in our selection are then identified by a new symbol: The Michelin Plate ⭥. Being chosen by the Michelin Inspectors for inclusion in the guide is a guarantee of quality in itself and the plate symbol highlights restaurants where you will have a good meal.

The presentation of the guide may have changed but our mission is still the same: to help you find the best restaurants and hotels on your travels. Please don't hesitate to contact us, as we are keen to hear your opinions on the establishments listed within these pages, as well as those you feel could be of interest for future editions.

We trust you will enjoy travelling with the 2017 edition of our Nordic Countries guide.

CONTENTS

Mondadori/hemis.fr

J.-C. Amiel/hemis.fr

J.-C. Amiel/hemis.fr

C. Gran/Folio Images/Getty Images

THE MICHELIN GUIDE'S COMMITMENTS

EXPERIENCED IN QUALITY

Whether they are in Japan, the USA, China or Europe, our inspectors use the same criteria to judge the quality of each and every hotel and restaurant that they visit. The Michelin guide commands a worldwide reputation thanks to the commitment we make to our readers - and we reiterate these below:

➡ ANONYMOUS INSPECTIONS

Our inspectors make regular and anonymous visits to hotels and restaurants to gauge the quality of products and services offered to an ordinary customer. They settle their own bill and may then introduce themselves and ask for more information about the establishment. Our readers' comments are also a valuable source of information, which we can follow up with a visit of our own.

➡ INDEPENDENCE

To remain totally objective for our readers, the selection is made with complete independence. Entry into the guide is free. All decisions are discussed with the Editor and our highest awards are considered at a European level.

foto@carstenmuller.com/G20

→ SELECTION AND CHOICE

The guide offers a selection of the best restaurants and hotels in every category of comfort and price. This is only possible because all the inspectors rigorously apply the same methods.

→ ANNUAL UPDATES

All the practical information, classifications and awards are revised and updated every year to give the most reliable information possible.

→ CONSISTENCY

The criteria for the classifications are the same in every country covered by the MICHELIN guide.

→ THE SOLE INTENTION OF MICHELIN IS TO MAKE YOUR TRAVELS SAFE AND ENJOYABLE.

QUALITY OF COOKING - THE AWARDS

❀❀❀ THREE MICHELIN STARS
Exceptional cuisine, worth a special journey!
Our highest award is given for the superlative cooking of chefs at the peak of their profession. The ingredients are exemplary, the cooking is elevated to an art form and their dishes are often destined to become classics.

❀❀ TWO MICHELIN STARS
Excellent cooking, worth a detour!
The personality and talent of the chef and their team is evident in the expertly crafted dishes, which are refined, inspired and sometimes original.

❀ ONE MICHELIN STAR
High quality cooking, worth a stop!
Using top quality ingredients, dishes with distinct flavours are carefully prepared to a consistently high standard.

☺ BIB GOURMAND
Good quality, good value cooking
'Bibs' are awarded for simple yet skilful cooking.

⑩ THE MICHELIN PLATE
Good cooking
Fresh ingredients, capably prepared: simply a good meal.

SEEK AND SELECT...

RESTAURANTS

Restaurants are listed by award. Within each award category, they are then ordered alphabetically.

❀❀❀ Three Stars: Exceptional cuisine, worth a special journey!

❀❀ Two Stars: Excellent cooking, worth a detour!

❀ One Star: High quality cooking, worth a stop!

🕥 Bib Gourmand: Good quality, good value cooking

🕽○ Michelin Plate: Good cooking

WHERE YOU ARE

Bottom of the page: country and town.

On the side: neighbourhood.

KADEAU ❀

CREATIVE • MINIMALIST

Baunevej 18, Vestre Sømark Pedersker, Åkirkeby (Southeast: 23 km by 38) ✉ 3720
TEL. 56 97 82 50 (booking essential) – www.kadeau.dk
Closed mid September-late April
Menu 800/1200 DKK (dinner only and lunch in July-August) (tasting menu only)

Chef:
Nicolai Nørregaard

Specialities:
Blue mussels, fermented wheat and elderberries. Hay-smoked celeriac, wild onion buds and burnt cheese. Caramelised buttermilk tart.

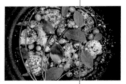

A remote beachside eatery with a superb sea panorama, which is best enjoyed from its terrace, although all tables have the view. The atmosphere is relaxed but they are serious about food here and the set no-choice menu of 5 or 8 dishes offers accomplished, original cooking with superbly balanced, contrasting flavours.

BORNHOLM

KEY WORDS

If you are looking for a specific type of establishment, these key words will help you make your choice more quickly.

• For hotels, the first word explains the establishment type (chain, business, luxury, etc.); the second one describes the décor (modern, stylish, design, etc.) and sometimes a third will be used to complete the picture.

• For restaurants, the first word relates to the type of cuisine and the second, to the atmosphere.

COMFORT

Level of comfort from 𝖃𝖃𝖃𝖃𝖃 to 𝖃.
Red: our most delightful places.

LOCATING THE ESTABLISHMENT

Location and coordinates on the town plan, with main sights

HOTELS

Hotels are listed by comfort, from 🏨🏨🏨 to 🏠. Within each comfort category, they are then ordered alphabetically.
Red: our most delightful places

FREDERIKSMINDE

COUNTRY HOUSE · ELEGANT · CLASSIC

Klosternakken 8 ✉ 4720
TEL. 55 90 90 30 – www.frederiksminde.com
Closed 23-26 December and 1-16 January
19 rm ☒ – ♦ 1145 DKK ♦♦ 1545 DKK
FREDERIKSMINDE ☺ – See restaurant listing

An attractive 19C house named after a former king of Denmark; it has a classic, understated style and offers superb views. Bedrooms are tastefully furnished, well-kept and comfortable; antiques and fine portraits feature.

FACILITIES & SERVICES

🏨	Hotel with a restaurant
♿	Wheelchair access
AC	Air conditioning (in all or part of the establishment)
🚭	Some facilities reserved for non-smokers
🍴	Outside dining available
🧖 🔥	Spa · Sauna · Exercise room
🏊	Swimming pool: outdoor or indoor
🌳 🎾	Garden or park · Tennis court
🏛	Conference room · Private dining room
🎭	Restaurant offering lower priced theatre menus
🚗 🅿	Valet parking · Garage · Car park
🚫	Credit cards not accepted
Ⓜ	Nearest metro station

OTHER SPECIAL FEATURES

⋙	Peaceful establishment
⋘	Great view
🍷	Particularly interesting wine list

9

Aflo/hemis.fr

DENMARK

AWARDS

COPENHAGEN

Denmark

J.-B. Rabouan/hemis.fr

Some cities overwhelm you, and give the impression that there's too much of them to take in. Not Copenhagen. Most of its key sights are neatly compressed within its central Slotsholmen 'island', an area that enjoyed its first golden age in the early seventeenth century in the reign of Christian IV, when it became a harbour of great consequence. It has canals on three sides and opposite the harbour is the area of Christianshavn, home of the legendary freewheeling 'free-town' community of Christiania. Further up from the centre are Nyhavn, the much-photographed canalside with brightly coloured buildings

where the sightseeing cruises leave from, and the elegant Frederiksstaden, whose wide streets contain palaces and museums. West of the centre is where Copenhageners love to hang out: the Tivoli Gardens, a kind of magical fairyland. Slightly more down-to-earth are the western suburbs of Vesterbro and Nørrebro, which were run-down areas given a street credible spit and polish for the 21C, and are now two of the trendiest districts. Once you've idled away some time in the Danish capital, you'll wonder why anyone might ever want to leave. With its waterfronts, quirky shops and cafés, the city presents a modern, user-friendly ambience – but it also boasts world class art collections, museums, and impressive parks, gardens and lakes, all of which bear the mark of an earlier time.

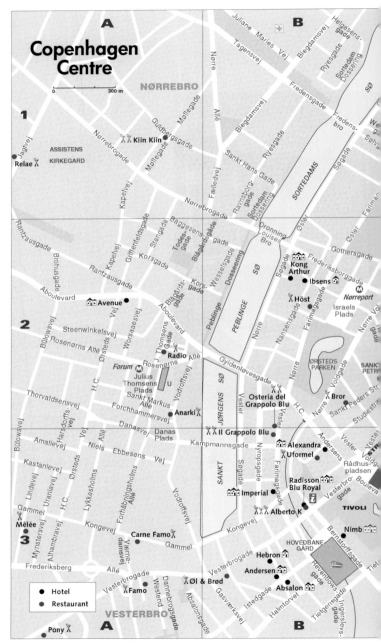

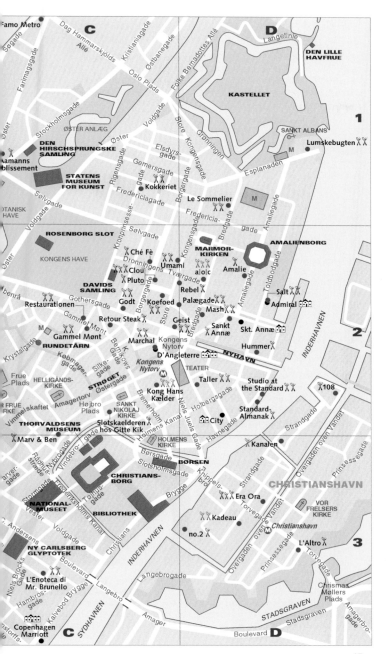

GERANIUM ✿✿✿

CENTRE

CREATIVE • DESIGN • ELEGANT   XxxX 🕸 ≼ A/C ⟷

Per Henrik Lings Allé 4 (8th Fl), Parken National Stadium
(3 km via Dag Hammaraskjölds Allé) ✉ 2100
TEL. 69 96 02 20 (booking essential) – **www**.geranium.dk
Closed 2 weeks Christmas, 2 weeks summer and Sunday-Tuesday

Menu 2000 DKK (surprise menu only)

Chef:
Rasmus Kofoed

Specialities:
Salted hake, parsley stems and
Finnish caviar in buttermilk. Grilled
pork, pickled pine and blackcurrant
leaves. Wood sorrel and woodruff.

With its panoramic park views, this luxurious restaurant feels as if it
is inviting the outside in, yet it's unusually located on the 8th floor
of the National Football Stadium. Modern techniques and the finest
organic and biodynamic ingredients are used to create beautiful,
pure and balanced dishes. The chefs invite you into the kitchen for
one of the courses.

A|O|C ✿✿

MODERN CUISINE • ELEGANT • ROMANTIC   XxX 🕸 ⟷

Dronningens Tvaergade 2 ✉ 1302 C **PLAN: D2**
Ⓜ Kongens Nytorv
TEL. 33 11 11 45 – **www**.restaurantaoc.dk
Closed July, 23-30 December, 1 January, Sunday and Monday

Menu 1300/1600 DKK (dinner only) (tasting menu only)

Specialities:
Baked onion with caviar and
elderflower sauce. Roe deer with
cherries, smoked marrow and
sorrel. Hazelnut ice cream with
burnt Jerusalem artichoke.

A spacious, simply decorated restaurant in the vaults of an eye-
catching 17C former seafarers building close to Nyhavn harbour and
the Royal Palace; owned and run by an experienced sommelier. Skilful,
well-judged and, at times, playful cooking has a Danish heart and
shows great originality as well as a keen eye for detail, flavour and
texture.

CLOU ❀

MODERN CUISINE • INTIMATE • NEIGHBOURHOOD XxX &

Borgergade 16 ⊠ 1300 K PLAN: C2
Ⓜ Kongens Nytorv
TEL. 36 16 30 00 (booking essential) – www.restaurant-clou.dk
Closed first 2 weeks August, 3 weeks late December-early January,
Sunday and Monday
Menu 1150/1950 DKK – Carte 545/1110 DKK (dinner only)

Chef:
Jonathan Berntsen
Specialities:
Scallops with Jerusalem artichoke
and black truffle. Quail with foie
gras and veal sweetbreads. Oialla
chocolate with caramel and berries.

A comfortable, intimate restaurant set over three converted shops,
with views into the kitchen from the street. Choose between 3, 5 or 7
course set menus and an à la carte: dishes are modern, attractive and
inventive, with interesting textures and flavours, and accompanying
wine matches. Service is assured.

ERA ORA ❀

ITALIAN • ELEGANT • INTIMATE XxX ⅋ ⌂

Overgaden Neden Vandet 33B ⊠ 1414 PLAN: D3
Ⓜ Christianshavn
TEL. 32 54 06 93 (booking essential) – www.era-ora.dk
Closed Christmas, Easter and Sunday
Menu 498/950 DKK (tasting menu only)

Specialities:
Crispy turbot with pistachio
and bell peppers. Guinea fowl,
gooseberries, cime di rapa and
chanterelles. Peach with tarragon
and liquorice.

A passionately run restaurant on a quaint cobbled street next to the
canal; inside it's grand, with high ceilings, a deep red colour scheme
and an air of formality. The set menu covers all regions of Italy and
the well-presented, modern dishes use top quality Italian produce in
vibrant flavour combinations.

FORMEL B ❀

MODERN CUISINE • FASHIONABLE • DESIGN XX 🕸 AC 🖵

Vesterbrogade 182-184, Frederiksberg
(2 km on Vesterbrogade) ✉ 1800 C
TEL. 33 25 10 66 (booking essential) – www.formelb.dk
Closed 24-26 December, 1 January and Sunday
Menu 850 DKK – Carte 410/850 DKK (dinner only)

Chef:
Kristian Arpe-Møller

Specialities:
Turbot with parsley, garlic and
braised veal tail. Pepper-glazed
sweetbread with carrots and
green rhubarb. Sea buckthorn 'en
surprise'.

Friendly staff create a relaxed environment at this appealing, modern
restaurant with its tree pictures and dark wood branches; ask for a
table by the kitchen on the lower level if you want to get close to the
action. Complex and original small plates are created with an assured
and confident touch.

KADEAU ❀

MODERN CUISINE • DESIGN • ELEGANT XX 🖵

Wildersgade 10B ✉ 1408 K PLAN: D3
Ⓜ Christianshavn
TEL. 33 25 22 23 (booking essential) – www.kadeau.dk
Closed 5 weeks July-August, 1 week Christmas
Menu 1850 DKK (dinner only and Saturday lunch)
(tasting menu only)

Chef:
Nicolai Nørregaard

Specialities:
Pickled vegetable terrine with
tomato water. Pork with sweet
onions and grilled blue cheese.
Fermented raspberries with
whitecurrant juice.

An intimate, welcoming restaurant with an open kitchen showcasing
cuisine and ingredients from Bornholm (an island just to the east of
the mainland from where the passionate owners originate). Precise
modern dishes feature well-balanced, flavoursome combinations,
many texture variations and fermented ingredients.

KIIN KIIN ❀

THAI • EXOTIC DÉCOR • INTIMATE

Guldbergsgade 21 ✉ 2200 N **PLAN: A1**
TEL. 35 35 75 55 (booking essential) – **www**.kiin.dk
Closed Christmas and Sunday
Menu 495/925 DKK (dinner only) (tasting menu only)

Specialities:
Frozen red curry with baby lobster and coriander. Beef with ginger and oyster sauce. Banana cake with salted ice cream and crispy coconut.

A charming restaurant, whose name means 'come and eat'. Start with refined versions of street food in the moody lounge, then head for the tasteful dining room decorated with golden Buddhas and fresh flowers. Menus offer modern, personal interpretations of Thai dishes with vibrant flavour combinations.

KOKKERIET ❀

MODERN CUISINE • INTIMATE • DESIGN

Kronprinsessegade 64 ✉ 1306 K **PLAN: C1**
TEL. 33 15 27 77 (booking essential) – **www**.kokkeriet.dk
Closed 24-26 December, 1 January and Sunday
Menu 900/1200 DKK (dinner only) (tasting menu only)

Chef:
David Johansen
Specialities:
Apple vinegar marinated celery with split pea purée. Roast poussin with Danish cheese and spruce. Sorrel sorbet with lemon mousse and caramel.

A discreet and elegant corner restaurant with two narrow, atmospheric rooms decorated in grey and black, and a collection of contemporary Danish artwork on display. Confidently executed, original cooking offers flavoursome, modern interpretations of classic Danish dishes. Service is smooth and unobtrusive.

KONG HANS KÆLDER ✿

CLASSIC FRENCH • ELEGANT • INTIMATE   XxX 𝓑 ⟷

Vingaardsstræde 6 ⊠ 1070 K **PLAN: C2**
Ⓜ Kongens Nytorv
TEL. 33 11 68 68 (booking essential) – **www**.konghans.dk
Closed 24 July-15 August, 24-28 December, 12-27 February,
11-12 April and Sunday-Tuesday
Menu 1700 DKK – Carte 1040/2510 DKK (dinner only)

Specialities:
Scallops, smoked butter and caviar.
Turbot baked in salt with ramsons
and champagne. Ice creams and
sorbets.

An intimate, historic restaurant in a beautiful vaulted Gothic cellar in
the heart of the city. Classic French cooking uses luxury ingredients
and has rich flavours, with signature dishes like Danish Black lobster.
There's a 7 course tasting menu and Gueridon trolleys add a theatrical
element to proceedings.

MARCHAL ✿

MODERN CUISINE • ELEGANT •
ROMANTIC   XX 𝓑 ⅏ 🖼 AⲤ

D'Angleterre Hotel • Kongens Nytorv 34 ⊠ 1050 K **PLAN: C2**
Ⓜ Kongens Nytorv
TEL. 33 12 00 95 – **www**.marchal.dk
Menu 300/500 DKK – Carte 510/2160 DKK

Specialities:
Squid with caviar and cucumber.
Chateaubriand en croûte with
truffle sauce. Raspberries &
peaches with rose hip and
champagne sabayon.

A stylish hotel restaurant overlooking the square and named after
the man who founded the hotel in 1755. Refined, Nordic-style cooking
has a classical French base; menus offer a range of small plates – 3
is about the right amount, or 4 if you're very hungry. Dinner also
includes an extensive caviar collection.

108 ✿

MODERN CUISINE • NEIGHBOURHOOD • DESIGN

Strandgade 108 ✉ 1401 K PLAN: D2
Ⓜ Christianshavn
TEL. 32 96 32 92 (booking advisable) – www.108.dk
Closed Christmas and 1 January
Carte 400/460 DKK (dinner only)

Chef:
Kristian Baumann

Specialities:
Rose hip marinated bleak roe with sweet salted plums. Raw lamb with last year's pickles. Rausu kombu ice cream with barley and blackcurrant wood oil.

A former whale meat warehouse with floor-to-ceiling windows and water views; bare concrete and a semi-open kitchen give it a cool Nordic style. There's a Noma alumnus in the kitchen and plenty of pickled, cured and fermented ingredients on the 'no rules' menu, from which you pick as many dishes as you like.

RELÆ ✿

MODERN CUISINE • MINIMALIST • FASHIONABLE

Jægersborggade 41 ✉ 2200N PLAN: A1
TEL. 36 96 66 09 (booking essential) – www.restaurant-relae.dk
Closed January and Sunday-Monday
Menu 475/895 DKK (dinner only and lunch Friday- Saturday)
(surprise menu only)

Specialities:
Green strawberries and marigold. Havervadgård lamb, romaine salad and tarragon. Yoghurt, chervil and lemon.

Book well in advance for a table at this simply styled restaurant, or grab a counter seat to watch the talented team in the open kitchen. Choose the 5 or 10 course surprise menu: unfussy, flavourful dishes come in original combinations and make innovative use of vegetables. Look in the drawers for your cutlery!

STUDIO AT THE STANDARD ✿

CREATIVE • FASHIONABLE • DESIGN   XX AC

Havnegade 44 ✉ 1058 K PLAN: D2
Ⓜ Kongens Nytorv
TEL. 72 14 88 08 (booking essential) – www.thestandardcph.dk
Closed 12-27 February, 23-26 December, Sunday and Monday
Menu 500/1000 DKK (dinner only and lunch Thursday-Saturday)
(tasting menu only)

Chef:
Torsten Vildgaard

Specialities:
Scallops with blackberries and
cream. Neck of Duroc pork with
peas and fermented garlic. Roast
corn with blackcurrants.

A showcase restaurant on the top floor of The Standard; sit at the
counter to watch the team at work. Dishes are brought to the table
by both the charming serving team and the passionate chefs. Classic
flavours and modern techniques intertwine in creative, often playful
dishes – and ingredients are top-notch.

L'ALTRO ☺

ITALIAN • INTIMATE • TRADITIONAL DÉCOR   X AC

Torvegade 62 ✉ 1400 K PLAN: D3
Ⓜ Christianshavn
TEL. 32 54 54 06 (booking essential) – www.laltro.dk
Closed 23-26 December and Sunday
Menu 430 DKK (dinner only) (tasting menu only)

A cosy, long-standing restaurant with a warm, rustic style; it
celebrates 'la cucina de la casa' – the homely Italian spirit of 'mama's
kitchen'. Regularly changing set menus feature tasty family recipes
from Umbria and Tuscany; dishes are appealing and rely on good
quality ingredients imported from Italy.

ANARKI 😶

TRADITIONAL CUISINE • NEIGHBOURHOOD •
BISTRO   ✗ ஃ

Vodroffsvej 47 ✉ 1900 C PLAN: A2
Ⓜ Forum
TEL. 22 13 11 34 – www.restaurant-anarki.dk
Closed July-August, Christmas, Sunday and Monday
Menu 385 DKK – Carte 260/425 DKK (dinner only)

An unassuming and proudly run neighbourhood bistro, just over the
water into Fredriksberg. The interesting menu of gutsy, flavourful
dishes draws inspiration from all over the world, so expect to see
words like ceviche, paella and burrata as well as bakskuld – with
plenty of offal and some great wines.

BROR 😶

REGIONAL CUISINE • BISTRO • RUSTIC   ✗ A/C

Skt Peders Strade 24A ✉ 1453 K PLAN: B2
Ⓜ Nørreport
TEL. 32 17 59 99 (booking essential) – www.restaurantbror.dk
Closed 3 weeks January, 24-26 December, Monday and Tuesday
Menu 395 DKK (dinner only) (tasting menu only)

Set on a narrow street in an older part of the city, this simple split-
level bistro is run by two keen young chefs and a friendly team. Set
4 course menu of rustic bistro dishes; extra courses can be added as
desired. Alternatively plump for the no-choice 5 course menu, which
comes with additional snacks.

CENTRE

ENOMANIA ☺

ITALIAN • WINE BAR • SIMPLE

Vesterbrogade 187 (2.5 km via Vesterbrogade) ✉ 1800 C
TEL. 33 23 60 80 (booking essential) – www.enomania.dk
Closed 22 December-8 January, 10-19 February, 29 March-2 April,
13-17 April, 8 July-7 August, 14-23 October, Saturday-Monday and
bank holidays
Menu 390 DKK – Carte 240/370 DKK (dinner only and lunch
Thursday-Friday)

A simple, bistro-style restaurant near Frederiksberg Park – its name
means 'Wine Mania'. The wine cellar comes with a table for tasting
and there's an excellent list of over 600 bins, mostly from Piedmont
and Burgundy. These are complemented by straightforward, tasty
Italian dishes from a daily 4 course menu.

FREDERIKS HAVE ☺

DANISH • NEIGHBOURHOOD • FAMILY

Smallegade 41, (entrance on Virginiavej)
(1.5 km. via Gammel Kongevej) ✉ 2000 F
Ⓜ Frederiksberg
TEL. 38 88 33 35 – www.frederikshave.dk
Closed 24 December-1 January, Easter and Sunday
Menu 295/395 DKK – Carte 340/530 DKK

A sweet neighbourhood restaurant hidden just off the main street in
a residential area. Sit inside – surrounded by flowers and vivid local
art – or outside, on the terrace. Well-presented, modern Danish dishes
have a classical base; tasty sweet and sour combinations feature. The
set lunches are great value.

KØDBYENS FISKEBAR 😊

SEAFOOD • SIMPLE • FASHIONABLE   X 🛖 P

Den Hvide Kødby, Flæsketorvet 100 (1 km via Halmtorvet) ✉ 1711 V
TEL. 32 15 56 56 – www.fiskebaren.dk
Closed 24-26 December and 1 January and lunch Monday to Friday
Carte 275/485 DKK

 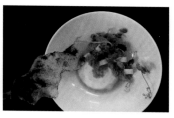

This buzzy, industrial-style restaurant is set, somewhat incongruously,
in a former butcher's shop in a commercial meat market. Concise
menus feature fresh, simply prepared seafood dishes which are
based around the latest catch; oysters are a speciality. The terrace is
a popular spot come summer.

MARV & BEN 😊

MODERN CUISINE • FRIENDLY • BISTRO   X

Snaregade 4 ✉ 1205 K PLAN: C2/3
Ⓜ Kongens Nytorv
TEL. 33 91 01 91 (booking advisable) – www.marvogben.dk
Closed Christmas, Sunday and Monday
Menu 350 DKK – Carte 300/500 DKK (dinner only)

A simple, two-floored restaurant down a cobbled street off the main
tourist track. Styling is stark and modern, with the kitchen on display
behind a glass wall. Gutsy, well-crafted dishes focus on produce
from the chefs' own fields. Service is friendly, with dishes sometimes
brought out by the chefs themselves.

MÊLÉE 😶

CENTRE

FRENCH • FRIENDLY • BISTRO

Martensens Allé 16 ✉ 1828 C **PLAN: A3**
Ⓜ Frederiksberg
TEL. 35 13 11 34 (booking essential) – **www**.melee.dk
Closed Christmas-New Year, Sunday and Monday
Menu 385 DKK – Carte 305/445 DKK (dinner only)

A bustling neighbourhood bistro with a friendly, laid-back atmosphere; run by an experienced team. Modern, country-style cooking is French-based but has Danish influences; menus might be concise but portions are generous and flavours are bold. An excellent range of wines from the Rhône Valley accompany.

PLUTO 😶

MEDITERRANEAN CUISINE • BISTRO • RUSTIC

Borgergade 16 ✉ 1300 K **PLAN: C2**
Ⓜ Kongens Nytorv
TEL. 33 16 00 16 – **www**.restaurantpluto.dk
Closed Sunday
Menu 450 DKK – Carte 190/470 DKK (dinner only)

An appealing restaurant in a residential area, with concrete pillars and an intentionally 'unfinished' feel – sit at wooden tables, at the long metal bar or at communal marble-topped tables. An enticing menu of small plates includes 'cheese' and 'sweets' sections; cooking is rustic, unfussy and flavoursome.

REBEL 😀

MODERN CUISINE • BISTRO • FASHIONABLE

Store Kongensgade 52 ✉ 1264 K PLAN: C/D2
Ⓜ Kongens Nytorv
TEL. 33 32 32 09 – www.restaurantrebel.dk
Closed 24 July-6 August, 2 weeks Christmas, Sunday and Monday
Carte 300/600 DKK (dinner only)

Located in a busy part of the city; a simply decorated, split-level
restaurant with closely set tables and a buzzy vibe – sit on the more
atmospheric ground floor, which looks into the kitchen. Choose 3 or
4 dishes from the list of 11; cooking is modern and refined, and relies
on Danish produce.

AAMANNS ETABLISSEMENT 🍴

DANISH • BISTRO • COSY

Øster Farimagsgade 12 ✉ 2100 Ø PLAN: C1
Ⓜ Nørreport
TEL. 35 55 33 10 (booking advisable) – www.aamanns.dk
Closed July, Christmas and dinner Sunday-Wednesday
Menu 295 DKK (lunch) – Carte 365/565 DKK

A cosy, contemporary restaurant with cheery service and an informal
atmosphere. Concise, seasonal menus blend traditional smørrebrød
with more modern 'small plates'. The 4 and 6 course dinner menus
come with wine pairings.

ALBERTO K 🍴

MODERN CUISINE • CHIC • ELEGANT   𝕏𝕩𝕏   ≼   A/C   P

Radisson Blu Royal Hotel • Hammerichsgade 1 ✉ 1611 V PLAN: B3
Ⓜ København Hovedbane Gård
TEL. 33 42 6161 – www.alberto-k.dk
Closed 1-8 January, 17 July-8 August, Easter, Christmas, Sunday
and bank holidays
Menu 750/950 DKK (dinner only) (tasting menu only)

Alberto K is located on the 20th floor of the Radisson Blu Royal and
is named after its first GM. It has a 1960s inspired, designer interior
and offers stunning city views. Monthly set menus offer modern
interpretations of classic dishes.

ALCHEMIST 🍴

CREATIVE • TRENDY • INTIMATE   𝕏𝕏   A/C

Århusgade 22 (3.5 km via Dag Hammerskjölds Allé off
Østerbrogade. 10 mins walk from Nordhavn station) ✉ 2100
TEL. 51 93 56 23 (booking essential) – www.restaurant-alchemist.dk
Closed 16 December-2 January, 2 July-2 August and
Sunday-Tuesday
Menu 3000 DKK (dinner only) (surprise menu only)

The ambitious chef transports diners to another world in this all-
encompassing culinary experience. Attentive staff, counter seating
and dramatic music provide the setting. The exciting, highly original
45 course menu includes wines.

AMALIE ⅋○

SMØRREBRØD • INTIMATE • RUSTIC

Amaliegade 11 ⊠ 1256 PLAN: D2
Ⓜ Kongens Nytorv
TEL. 33 12 88 10 (booking essential) – www.restaurantamalie.dk
Closed 24 December-2 January, Easter, Sunday and bank holidays
Menu 269 DKK – Carte 219/322 DKK (lunch only)

Charming 18C townhouse by Amalienborg Palace, with two tiny, cosy rooms filled with old paintings and elegant porcelain. The authentic Danish menu offers a large choice of herring, salmon and salads. Service is warm and welcoming.

AMASS ⅋○

DANISH • MINIMALIST • FRIENDLY

Refshalevej 153 (3 km via Torvgade and Prinsessgade) ⊠ 1432
TEL. 43 58 43 30 (booking essential) – www.amassrestaurant.com
Closed 24-25 December, 1 January, Sunday and Monday
Menu 395/850 DKK (dinner only and lunch Friday-Saturday)

A large restaurant just outside the city. It has an urban, industrial feel courtesy of high graffitied concrete walls and huge windows overlooking the old docks. Prices and the authenticity of ingredients are key; cooking is modern Danish.

CARNE FAMO 🍴⃝

ITALIAN • MINIMALIST • FRIENDLY

Gammel Kongevej 51 ✉ 1610 V **PLAN: A3**
TEL. 33 22 22 50 (booking essential) – **www**.famo.dk
Closed 2 weeks summer, Christmas and Sunday

Menu 450 DKK – Carte 370/445 DKK (dinner only)

A laid-back restaurant with the style of a modern osteria. The extensive menu offers authentic, rustic Italian dishes made with fresh seasonal ingredients – and there are plenty of well-priced wines on the all-Italian wine list.

CHÉ FÈ 🍴⃝

ITALIAN • SIMPLE • NEIGHBOURHOOD

Borgergade 17a ✉ 1300 K **PLAN: C2**
Ⓜ Kongens Nytorv
TEL. 33 11 17 21 (booking essential) – **www**.chefe.dk
Closed 21-26 December, 1 January, 9-31 July and Easter Monday

Menu 350/490 DKK – Carte 430/485 DKK (dinner only)

An unassuming façade conceals an appealing trattoria with pastel hues and coffee sack curtains. Menus offer authentic Italian classics, including homemade pastas; virtually all ingredients are imported from small, organic producers.

L' ENOTECA DI MR. BRUNELLO ⅋〇

ITALIAN • ELEGANT • NEIGHBOURHOOD   XX ⅋

Rysensteensgade 16 ⌧ 1564 K **PLAN: C3**
TEL. 33 11 47 20 – **www**.lenoteca.dk
Closed 1 July-15 August, Easter, Christmas, Sunday, Monday and
bank holidays
Menu 495 DKK – Carte 495/755 DKK (dinner only)

Tucked away near the Tivoli Gardens and run by passionate,
experienced owners. Refined, classic Italian cooking uses good
quality produce imported from Italy. The good value Italian wine
list has over 150 different Brunello di Montalcinos.

FAMO ⅋〇

ITALIAN • BISTRO • NEIGHBOURHOOD   X

Saxogade 3 ⌧ 1662 **PLAN: A3**
TEL. 33 23 22 50 (booking essential) – **www**.famo.dk
Closed Christmas and early January
Menu 380 DKK (dinner only) (tasting menu only)

A modern, simply styled Italian restaurant serving rustic cooking.
Extensive daily menus are presented orally: they offer a choice of 8
antipasti, followed by tasty homemade pastas, generous main courses
and authentic desserts.

FAMO METRO 🍴

ITALIAN • BISTRO • SIMPLE   X AC

Øster Søgade 114 ✉ 2100 Ø PLAN: C1
TEL. 35 55 66 30 – **www**.famo.dk
Closed 2 weeks summer and Sunday
Menu 400 DKK (dinner only)

A neighbourhood restaurant with floor to ceiling windows,
overlooking Sortedams Lake. Well-priced daily changing menu;
classic Italian dishes are authentic and full of flavour. Service is helpful
and friendly.

56° 🍴

DANISH • RUSTIC • ROMANTIC   X 🛖 🍽

Krudtløbsvej 8 (2.5 km. via Torvgade, Prinsessgade and
Refshalevej) ✉ 1439 K
TEL. 31 16 32 05 – **www**.restaurant56grader.dk
Closed Christmas, Sunday dinner and Monday
Menu 220/375 DKK

A sweet, rustic restaurant, unusually set within the 1.5m thick walls of
a 17C gunpowder store. Flavoursome Danish cooking mixes modern
and traditional elements and keeps Nordic produce to the fore. The
large garden is a hit.

GAMMEL MØNT ⫶⃝

TRADITIONAL CUISINE • COSY • FRIENDLY   ✗✗

Gammel Mønt 41 ✉ 1117 K PLAN: C2
Ⓜ Kongens Nytorv
TEL. 33 15 10 60 – **www**.glmoent.dk
Closed July, Christmas, Easter, Saturday-Monday and bank holidays
Menu 425/565 DKK – Carte 595/920 DKK (lunch only and dinner Wednesday-Friday)

A part-timbered house in the heart of the city; dating back to 1739, it sports a striking shade of deep terracotta. The menu celebrates Danish classics and dishes are hearty, gutsy and reassuringly traditional; try the pickled herrings.

GEIST ⫶⃝

MODERN CUISINE • DESIGN • TRENDY   ✗✗ 🏠 AC

Kongens Nytorv 8 ✉ 1050 K PLAN: C2
Ⓜ Kongens Nytorv
TEL. 33 13 37 13 – **www**.restaurantgeist.dk
Closed 23-26 December and 1 January
Carte 385/465 DKK (dinner only)

A lively, fashionable restaurant with an open kitchen and a sexy nightclub vibe, set in a striking red-brick property with floor to ceiling windows – in a superb spot overlooking the square. Cleverly crafted dishes display a light touch; 4 should suffice.

GODT ⅱ○

CLASSIC CUISINE • FRIENDLY • FAMILY   ⅩⅩ

Gothersgade 38 ⊠ 1123 K PLAN: C2
Ⓜ Kongens Nytorv
TEL. 33 15 21 22 – www.restaurant-godt.dk
Closed mid July to mid August, Christmas-New Year, Easter,
Sunday, Monday and bank holidays

Menu 520/680 DKK (dinner only) (tasting menu only)

 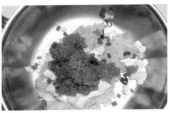

A stylish restaurant seating just 20, where the service is particularly
friendly. Traditional French and European daily menus – of 3, 4 and
5 courses – are formed around the latest market produce. Old WWII
shells act as candle holders.

GORILLA ⅱ○

MODERN CUISINE • BRASSERIE • SIMPLE   Ⅹ 🏠

Flæsketorvet 63 (1 km via Halmtorvet) ⊠ 1711 V
TEL. 33 33 83 30 – www.restaurantgorilla.dk
Closed 23-25 December, Sunday and bank holidays
Menu 375/450 DKK – Carte 115/360 DKK (dinner only)

A buzzy, canteen-style restaurant in the meatpacking district; the
stone floor, zinc ducting and large windows create an industrial feel.
The menu offers something for everyone; dishes are well-presented,
tasty and designed for sharing.

HÖST ‖○

MODERN CUISINE • FRIENDLY • RUSTIC

Nørre Farimagsgade 41 ✉ 1364 K PLAN: B2
Ⓜ Nørreport
TEL. 89 93 84 09 – www.cofoco.dk/en/restaurants/hoest
Closed 24 December, 1 January and lunch Sunday-Wednesday
Menu 295/495 DKK

A busy neighbourhood bistro with fun staff and a lively atmosphere; sit
in the Garden Room. The great value monthly set menu comprises 3
courses but comes with lots of extras. Cooking is modern Nordic,
seasonal and boldly flavoured.

HUMMER ‖○

SEAFOOD • FRIENDLY • SIMPLE

Nyhavn 63A ✉ 1051 K PLAN: D2
Ⓜ Kongens Nytorv
TEL. 33 33 03 39 – www.restauranthummer.dk
Menu 425 DKK – Carte 220/410 DKK

Lobster is the mainstay of the menu at this restaurant, situated among
the brightly coloured buildings on the famous Nyhavn strip. Enjoy a
meal on the sunny terrace or in the modish, nautically styled dining
room.

IL GRAPPOLO BLU 🍴

ITALIAN • RUSTIC • COSY   XX

Vester Farimagsgade 35 ⊠ 1606 V PLAN: B3
Ⓜ Nørreport
TEL. 33 11 57 20 – www.igb.dk
Closed July, Easter, Christmas, New Year, Sunday and Monday
Menu 450/750 DKK – Carte 385/440 DKK (dinner only)

A cosy restaurant with dark panelling and ornate carvings. 8 and 14 course tasting menus: well-prepared, authentic Italian dishes include appealing antipasti and tasty pastas. The wine list features over 200 different Brunello di Montalcinos.

KANALEN 🍴

DANISH • BISTRO • COSY   X ⪮ 🏠 ⟷ P

Wilders Plads 1-3 ⊠ 1403 K PLAN: D3
Ⓜ Christianshavn
TEL. 32 95 13 30 (booking essential) – www.restaurant-kanalen.dk
Closed Sunday and bank holidays
Menu 250/400 DKK – Carte 350/465 DKK

Former Harbour Police office with a lovely terrace, in a delightful canalside setting. The dining room has a contemporary edge and French windows facing the water. The chefs in the tiny open kitchen prepare a well-balanced Danish menu with light French and Asian touches, which is served by a charming team.

KOEFOED ⓘ○

CREATIVE • INTIMATE • ROMANTIC

Landegreven 3 ✉ 1301 K PLAN: C2
Ⓜ Kongens Nytorv
TEL. 56 48 22 24 (booking essential at dinner) –
www.restaurant-koefoed.dk
Closed 22 December-2 January, Sunday and Monday
Menu 295/495 DKK – Carte 410/500 DKK

An intimate collection of rooms in a former coal cellar, where
everything from the produce to the glassware celebrates the island
of Bornholm. Modern Danish cooking with deconstructed smørrebrød
at lunch and an impressive range of bordeaux.

LUMSKEBUGTEN ⓘ○

TRADITIONAL CUISINE • COSY •
CLASSIC DÉCOR

Esplanaden 21 ✉ 1263 K PLAN: D1
TEL. 33 15 60 29 – www.lumskebugten.dk
Closed 3 weeks July, Christmas, Easter, Sunday and bank holidays
Menu 325/475 DKK – Carte 400/735 DKK

A restored quayside pavilion dating from 1854; the Royal Family
occasionally dine here. A series of small rooms are adorned with
maritime memorabilia and paintings. Local menus offer a wide
selection of traditional fish dishes.

MASH ⧉

MEATS AND GRILLS • BRASSERIE •
CLASSIC DÉCOR

XX 🕸 AC ⇔

Bredgade 20 ✉ 1260 K PLAN: D2
Ⓜ Kongens Nytorv
TEL. 33 13 93 00 (booking essential at dinner) – www.mashsteak.dk
Closed 24 December-2 January, lunch Saturday and Sunday

Carte 355/810 DKK

A smart, lively, American-style steakhouse with a trendy cocktail bar
and aged meats on display; sit in the rear room with its red leather
booths. Classic steak dishes come with a choice of sides and sauces.
French and American wine list.

MIELCKE & HURTIGKARL ⧉

CREATIVE • ELEGANT • EXOTIC DÉCOR

XxX

Runddel 1 (2 km via Veseterbrogade and Frederiksberg Allé)
✉ 2000 C
TEL. 38 34 84 36 (booking essential) – www.mhcph.com
Closed Christmas-New Year, Sunday and Monday

Menu 800/1100 DKK (dinner only)

Charming 1744 orangery with a fire-lit terrace, set in a delightful spot
in Frederiksberg Gardens. The walls are painted with garden scenes
and there are backing tracks of birdsong. The ambitious, modern set
menus use lots of herbs and vegetables from the gardens. Service is
wonderfully attentive.

NO.2 ⚏

MODERN CUISINE • DESIGN • FASHIONABLE   ✗ ⪕ 🏠 AC

Nicolai Eigtveds Gade 32 ✉ 1402 C PLAN: D3
Ⓜ Christianshaven
TEL. 33 11 11 68 – www.nummer2.dk
Closed 2 weeks in July, 23-27 December, 1 January, Saturday lunch
and Sunday
Menu 250 DKK (weekday lunch)/450 DKK – Carte 300/525 DKK

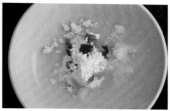

Set among smart offices and apartments on the edge of the dock, is
this elegant restaurant; the sister to a|o|c. Fresh, flavoursome small
plates focus on quality Danish ingredients – be sure to try the cheeses
and cured hams.

ØL & BRØD ⚏

MODERN CUISINE • NEIGHBOURHOOD • COSY   ✗

Viktoriagade 6 ✉ 1620 PLAN: B3
Ⓜ København Hovedbane Gård
TEL. 33 31 44 22 (booking essential) – www.ologbrod.com
Closed Monday
Menu 500 DKK (dinner) – Carte lunch 280/440 DKK (lunch only and
dinner Thursday-Saturday)

A cosy, hip neighbourhood restaurant where the emphasis is as much
on aquavit and craft beers as it is on the refined and flavourful modern
food. Lunch sees smørrebrød taken to a new level, while dinner offers
a choice of 3 or 6 courses.

OSTERIA DEL GRAPPOLO BLU 🍴

ITALIAN • FRIENDLY • TRADITIONAL DÉCOR XX

Vester Farimagsgade 37 ⊠ 1606 V PLAN: B2/3
Ⓜ Nørreport
TEL. 33 12 57 20 – www.osteria.dk
Closed July, Easter, Christmas, New Year, Sunday and Monday
Menu 450/750 DKK – Carte 385/440 DKK (dinner only)

The more informal counterpart to Il Grappolo Blu; a laid-back restaurant with smart 'osteria' styling. Authentic homemade dishes have their roots in southern Italy; breads, pastas and ice creams are made on the premises daily.

PALÆGADE 🍴

SMØRREBRØD • FRIENDLY • SIMPLE XX 🛖

Palægade 8 ⊠ 1261 K PLAN: C2
Ⓜ Kongens Nytorv
TEL. 70 82 82 88 – www.palaegade.dk
Closed Christmas-New Year, Monday dinner and Sunday
Menu 495 DKK – Carte 350/515 DKK

More than 40 classic smørrebrød are available at lunch – with plenty of local beer and schnapps to accompany them. Things become more formal in the evenings, when they serve highly seasonal dishes in a traditional Northern European style.

PONY iO

DANISH • BISTRO • NEIGHBOURHOOD

Vesterbrogade 135 ✉ 1620 V PLAN: A3
TEL. 33 22 10 00 (booking essential) – www.ponykbh.dk
Closed July-August, 1 week in Christmas and Monday
Menu 450 DKK – Carte 390/495 DKK (dinner only)

Neighbourhood restaurant with chatty service and a buzzy vibe: sit at high tables opposite the kitchen or on retro seats in the small dining room. Choose 4 of the tasty, original dishes; refined, modern cooking has a 'nose-to-tail' approach.

RADIO iO

MODERN CUISINE • MINIMALIST • NEIGHBOURHOOD

Julius Thomsens Gade 12 ✉ 1632 V PLAN: A2
Ⓜ Forum
TEL. 25 10 27 33 (booking essential) – www.restaurantradio.dk
Closed 3 weeks summer, 2 weeks Christmas-New Year, Sunday and Monday
Menu 300/400 DKK (dinner only and lunch Friday-Saturday) (tasting menu only)

An informal restaurant with an unfussy urban style, wood-clad walls and cool anglepoise lighting. Oft-changing set menus feature full-flavoured, good value dishes and use organic ingredients grown in the chefs' nearby fields.

RESTAURATIONEN ⅟○

CLASSIC CUISINE • CHIC • ROMANTIC   ✕✕ ⌘

Møntergade 19 ✉ 1116 K **PLAN: C2**
Ⓜ Kongens Nytorv
TEL. 33 14 94 95 – **www**.restaurationen.com
Closed Easter, early July-late August, Christmas-New Year,
Sunday and Monday
Menu 575 DKK (dinner only)

This restaurant celebrated 25 years in 2016, and is run by a well-known
chef who also owns the next door wine bar. Modern Danish dishes are
created with quality local produce. The dining room displays some
impressive vibrant modern art.

RETOUR STEAK ⅟○

MEATS AND GRILLS • BISTRO • FRIENDLY   ⅟

Ny Østergade 21 ✉ 1101 K **PLAN: C2**
Ⓜ Kongens Nytorv
TEL. 33 33 83 30 (booking essential) – **www**.retoursteak.dk
Menu 450 DKK – Carte 345/530 DKK (dinner only)

A relaxed, informal restaurant with a stark white interior and
contrasting black furnishings. A small menu offers simply prepared
grills, good quality American rib-eye steaks and an affordable
selection of wines.

SALT ᵗᵐ○

MODERN CUISINE • DESIGN • FASHIONABLE   ✗✗ 🚇 🅿

Admiral Hotel • Toldbodgade 24-28 ✉ 1253K PLAN: D2
Ⓜ Kongens Nytorv
TEL. 33 74 14 44 – **www**.salt.dk
Menu 395 DKK – Carte 500/510 DKK

A bright and airy hotel restaurant; its vast old timber beams a reminder
of the building's previous life as a granary and its harbourside terrace
a great spot in the summer months. Extensive menus offer interesting
modern cooking.

SANKT ANNÆ ᵗᵐ○

SMØRREBRØD • COSY • CLASSIC DÉCOR   ✗ 🚇 ⛱

Sankt Annæ Plads 12 ✉ 1250 K PLAN: D2
Ⓜ Kongens Nytorv
TEL. 33 12 54 97 (booking essential) –
www.restaurantsanktannae.dk
Closed Easter, 18 July-7 August, Christmas-New Year, Sunday and
bank holidays

Carte 224/368 DKK (lunch only)

An attractive terraced building with a traditional, rather quaint
interior. There's a seasonal à la carte and a daily blackboard menu:
prices can vary so check before ordering. The lobster and shrimp –
fresh from local fjords – are a hit.

SLOTSKÆLDEREN HOS GITTE KIK ⁇

SMØRREBRØD • FAMILY • TRADITIONAL DÉCOR

Fortunstræde 4 ⊠ 1065 K PLAN: C2
Ⓜ Kongens Nytorv
TEL. 33 11 15 37 (booking essential) – **www**.slotskaelderen.dk
Closed July, Sunday, Monday and bank holidays

Carte 205/340 DKK (lunch only)

Set in a 1797 building and family-run since 1910, this established restaurant sets the benchmark for this type of cuisine. The rustic inner is filled with portraits and city scenes. Go to the counter to see the full selection of smørrebrød.

LE SOMMELIER ⁇

FRENCH • BRASSERIE • TRADITIONAL DÉCOR   ⁇⁇ ⁇ ⁇

Bredgade 63-65 ⊠ 1260 K PLAN: D1
TEL. 33 11 45 15 – **www**.lesommelier.dk
Closed 22 December-4 January, Easter and lunch Saturday and Sunday

Carte 435/585 DKK

Attractively refurbished brasserie in the heart of the Old Town, where French wine posters and a superb wine list hint at the owners' passion. The small à la carte features classic French dishes and is supplemented by a daily set menu.

STANDARD - ALMANAK ⅼ○

MODERN CUISINE • FASHIONABLE ✗ 🏠

Havnegade 44 ✉ 1058 PLAN: D2
Ⓜ Kongens Nytorv
TEL. 72 14 88 08 (bookings advisable at dinner) –
www.thestandardcph.dk
Closed Christmas and New Year
Menu 409/500 DKK – Carte 268/545 DKK

In a waterfront setting, on the ground floor of an impressive art deco former customs building. At lunch, it's all about tasty smørrebrød, while dinner sees a concise menu of updated Danish classics. An open kitchen adds to the theatre.

TALLER ⅼ○

WORLD CUISINE • FASHIONABLE • FRIENDLY ✗✗

Tordenskjoldsgade 11 ✉ 1055 K PLAN: D2
Ⓜ Kongens Nytorv
TEL. 72 14 08 71 (booking essential) – **www**.restaurant-taller.dk
Closed 23-27 December, 1-10 January and Sunday-Tuesday
Menu 375 DKK (lunch)/1175 DKK (dinner only and lunch Friday-Saturday)

Colourful and creative modern interpretations of Venezuelan dishes are served at this stylish restaurant, whose name translates as 'workshop' in Spanish – take a seat at the open kitchen counter to see the chef-owner at work close up.

UFORMEL ⅰ◯

MODERN CUISINE • FASHIONABLE • TRENDY ✗ AC ⇳

Studiestraede 69 ⊠ 1554 K **PLAN: B3**
Ⓜ København Hovedbane Gård
TEL. 70 99 9111 (booking essential) – **www**.uformel.dk
Closed 24-27 December and 1-2 January
Menu 775 DKK – Carte 440/660 DKK (dinner only)

The informal sister of Formel B, with gold table-tops, black cutlery, a smart open kitchen and a cocktail bar (a lively spot at the weekend!) Dishes are tasting plates and all are the same price; 4-6 is about the right amount.

UMAMI ⅰ◯

ASIAN • FASHIONABLE • DESIGN ✗✗ AC ⇳

Store Kongensgade 59 ⊠ 1264 **PLAN: C/D2**
Ⓜ Kongens Nytorv
TEL. 33 38 75 00 – **www**.restaurantumami.dk
Closed 24 December-2 January, Easter Monday and Sunday
Menu 650 DKK – Carte 350/480 DKK (dinner only)

Attractive building with a large cocktail bar and lounge on the ground floor, and an elegant upper level boasting a stylish, atmospheric dining room, a sushi counter and an open kitchen. Cooking is Japanese, with a European slant.

D'ANGLETERRE

LUXURY • HISTORIC • CONTEMPORARY

⚐ ♿ ▣ 🖥 spa ⁂ ⅃⅄ A/C 🏊

Kongens Nytorv 34 ✉ 1050 K PLAN: C2
Ⓜ Kongens Nytorv
TEL. 33 12 00 95 – **www**.dangleterre.com
90 rm – ♀ 2750/3500 DKK ♀♀ 5000/6500 DKK, ☕ 285 DKK – 30 suites
MARCHAL ✿ – See restaurant listing

Smartly refurbished landmark hotel dating back over 250 years. Well-
equipped bedrooms come in various shapes and sizes; it's worth
paying the extra for a Royal Square view. Unwind in the basement
spa or the chic champagne bar.

COPENHAGEN MARRIOTT

LUXURY • BUSINESS • MODERN

⇐ ⚐ ♿ ⁂ ⅃⅄ A/C 🏊 🅿

Kalvebod Brygge 5 ✉ 1560 V PLAN: C3
TEL. 88 33 99 00 – **www**.copenhagenmarriott.dk
402 rm – ♀ 1899/5000 DKK ♀♀ 1899/5000 DKK, ☕ 230 DKK
– 9 suites

Striking waterfront hotel; take in the views from the terrace or from
the floor to ceiling windows in the large lounge-bar. Bright, spacious
bedrooms are handsomely appointed and afford canal or city views.
The popular American grill restaurant offers steaks, chops and
seafood, and has a lively open kitchen.

NIMB

LUXURY • DESIGN • ROMANTIC

Bernstorffsgade 5 ✉ 1577 V PLAN: B3
Ⓜ København Hovedbane Gård
TEL. 88 70 00 00 – www.nimb.dk
17 rm ☕ – 🛉 2800/3290 DKK 🛉🛉 4200/5900 DKK

An ornate, Moorish-style building dating from 1909, situated in Tivoli
Gardens. Smart, stylish bedrooms are sympathetically designed and
well-equipped – most overlook the gardens. Eat in the lively bar and
grill, the formal French brasserie or the contemporary restaurant. The
rustic wine bar offers over 2,000 bottles – and you can enjoy Danish
open sandwiches and schnapps in Fru Nimb.

ADMIRAL

BUSINESS • HISTORIC • MODERN

Toldbodgade 24-28 ✉ 1253 K PLAN: D2
Ⓜ Kongens Nytorv
TEL. 33 74 14 14 – www.admiralhotel.dk
366 rm – 🛉 1335/1825 DKK 🛉🛉 1535/2925 DKK, ☕ 150 DKK
SALT – See restaurant listing

An impressive 1787 former grain-drying warehouse, with an appealing
maritime theme running throughout. Bedrooms feature vintage
beams and bespoke wood furniture and have city or harbour views;
opt for one of the duplex suites.

IMPERIAL

BUSINESS • TRADITIONAL • MODERN

Vester Farimagsgade 9 ⊠ 1606 V PLAN: B3
Ⓜ København Hovedbane Gård
TEL. 33 12 80 00 – **www**.imperialhotel.dk
304 rm – ♚ 1300/2300 DKK ♛ 1600/2800 DKK, ☕ 170 DKK – 1 suite

A well-known hotel, geared up for conferences and centrally located
on a wide city thoroughfare. Bedrooms are particularly spacious and
have a subtle Danish style. The contemporary restaurant features
a brightly coloured Italian theme wall and serves Italian dishes to
match.

ISLAND

BUSINESS • CHAIN • MODERN

Kalvebod Brygge 53 (via Kalvebod Brygge) ⊠ 1560 V
TEL. 33 38 96 00 – **www**.copenhagenisland.dk
326 rm – ♚ 850/3050 DKK ♛ 950/3250 DKK, ☕ 185 DKK

Contemporary glass and steel hotel set just outside the city, on a man-
made island in the harbour. Bedrooms are well-equipped – some are
allergy friendly and some have balconies; choose a water view over
a city view. The stylish multi-level lounge-bar and restaurant serves
a wide-ranging international menu.

KONG ARTHUR

TOWNHOUSE • TRADITIONAL • CLASSIC

Nørre Søgade 11 ⊠ 1370 K PLAN: B2
Ⓜ Nørreport
TEL. 33 11 12 12 – www.arthurhotels.dk
155 rm – 🛉 1125/1895 DKK 🛉🛉 1895/2280 DKK, ☲ 175 DKK

Four 1882 buildings set around a courtyard, in an elegant residential avenue close to Peblinge Lake. Well-equipped bedrooms have a high level of facilities. Relax in the smart Thai spa and enjoy complimentary drinks from 5-6pm.

RADISSON BLU ROYAL

BUSINESS • DESIGN

Hammerichsgade 1 ⊠ 1611 V PLAN: B3
Ⓜ København Hovedbane Gård
TEL. 33 42 60 00 – www.radissonblu.com/royalhotel-copenhagen
260 rm – 🛉 995/4895 DKK 🛉🛉 1195/5095 DKK, ☲ 195 DKK – 2 suites
ALBERTO K – See restaurant listing

Spacious hotel designed by Arne Jacobson, with extensive conference and fitness facilities. Bedrooms have a typical Scandinavian style – the largest are the double-aspect corner rooms; Number 606 still has its original furnishings. Dine informally in all-day Café Royal or enjoy panoramic views from Alberto K.

ABSALON

FAMILY • DESIGN

Helgolandsgade 15 ✉ 1653 V PLAN: B3
Ⓜ København Hovedbane Gård
TEL. 33 24 22 11 – **www**.absalon-hotel.dk
162 rm 🛏 – 👤 1150/2100 DKK 👫 1300/2850 DKK – 2 suites

A family-run hotel located close to the railway station and furnished with vibrantly coloured fabrics. Elegant, comfortable bedrooms feature an 'artbox' on the wall which celebrates an aspect of Danish design such as Lego or porcelain.

ALEXANDRA

BOUTIQUE HOTEL • BUSINESS • DESIGN

H.C. Andersens Boulevard 8 ✉ 1553 V PLAN: B3
Ⓜ København Hovedbane Gård
TEL. 33 74 44 94 – **www**.hotelalexandra.dk
Closed Christmas
61 rm – 👤 1500/2250 DKK 👫 1850/2600 DKK, 🛏 138 DKK

A well-run, late Victorian hotel in the city centre, with a contrastingly modern interior. Bedrooms are individually styled and there's an entire 'allergy friendly' floor; the 12 'Design' rooms are styled by famous Danish designers.

ANDERSEN

FAMILY • DESIGN

Helgolandsgade 12 ✉ 1653 **PLAN: B3**

Ⓜ København Hovedbane Gård
TEL. 33 31 46 10 – **www**.andersen-hotel.dk
Closed 22-26 December
77 rm ☞ – 👤 1075/2000 DKK 👥 1275/3200 DKK

Bright and funky boutique styling is the hallmark of this hotel, where the individually furnished bedrooms are classified as 'Cool', 'Brilliant', 'Wonderful' and 'Amazing'. Honesty bar in reception; complimentary glass of wine, 5–6pm.

AVENUE

BUSINESS • FAMILY • MODERN
🛁 🅿

Åboulevard 29 ✉ 1960 C **PLAN: A2**
Ⓜ Forum
TEL. 35 37 31 11 – **www**.brochner-hotels.dk
Closed Christmas
68 rm – 👤 895/6000 DKK 👥 1095/6200 DKK, ☞ 160 DKK

Well-maintained, family-run hotel dating back to 1899. Relax around the central bar in the smart modern lounge or out on the courtyard patio. Bedrooms have a bright, crisp style and feature striking Philippe Starck lights.

CITY

BUSINESS • TRADITIONAL • GRAND LUXURY

Peder Skrams Gade 24 ⊠ 1054 K PLAN: D2
Ⓜ Kongens Nytorv
TEL. 33 13 06 66 – www.hotelcity.dk
81 rm ⌑ – ♦ 895/2295 DKK ♦♦ 1195/2595 DKK

Modern hotel in a quiet street between the city and the docks.
Bedrooms boast monochrome Jan Persson jazz photos and Jacobsen
armchairs. Designer furniture features throughout and there's an eye-
catching water feature in the lobby.

SKT. ANNÆ

BUSINESS • TOWNHOUSE • COSY

Sankt Annæ Plads 18-20 ⊠ 1250 K PLAN: D2
Ⓜ Kongens Nytorv
TEL. 33 96 20 00 – www.hotelsanktannae.dk
154 rm – ♦ 1090/1990 DKK ♦♦ 1290/2390 DKK, ⌑ 195 DKK – 1 suite

Three Victorian townhouses not far from the bustling harbourside
of Nyhavn. Ask for a 'Superior' bedroom for more space and quiet;
Room 601 is the best – it's accessed via the roof terrace and has its
own balcony overlooking the rooftops.

HEBRON

TRADITIONAL • FAMILY • FUNCTIONAL

Helgolandsgade 4 ✉ 1653 V PLAN: B3
Ⓜ København Hovedbane Gård
TEL. 33 316906 – www.hebron.dk
Closed 22 December-2 January
99 rm ☲ – ♦ 700/1900 DKK ♦♦ 900/2100 DKK – 2 suites

A smart hotel behind a Victorian façade – this was one of the city's biggest when it opened in 1899 and some original features still remain. There's a comfy lounge and a grand breakfast room; well-kept bedrooms range in shape and size.

IBSENS

HISTORIC • FAMILY • PERSONALISED
🅿

Vendersgade 23 ✉ 1363 K PLAN: B2
Ⓜ Nørreport
TEL. 33 131913 – www.arthurhotels.dk
118 rm ☲ – ♦ 880/2445 DKK ♦♦ 1230/2820 DKK

A simply, brightly furnished hotel with a relaxed, bohemian feel: the little sister to Kong Arthur. The small bar serves breakfast, as well as complimentary drinks from 5-6pm. Bedrooms are well-kept – 'Tiny' really are compact.

PAUSTIAN 🍴

DANISH • FASHIONABLE • DESIGN   XX ⋜ 🏠 P

Kalkbrænderiløbskaj 2 (North: 4 km by Folke Bernadottes Allé) ✉ 2150 Ø
TEL. 39 18 55 01 (booking advisable) – **www**.restaurantpaustian.dk
Closed July, 23 December-14 January and Sunday

Carte 420/435 DKK (lunch only)

A friendly, informal restaurant set in an impressive harbourside building designed by renowned architect Jørn Utzon. Traditional Danish cooking with French touches; watch the chefs at work in the open kitchen.

DEN RØDE COTTAGE ✿

DANISH • DESIGN   XX 🏠 ⬭

Strandvejen 550 (North: 12 km by Folke Bernadottes Allé and Road 2) ✉ 2930
TEL. 39 90 46 14 (booking essential) – **www**.denroedecottage.dk
Closed 22 December-22 February and Sunday October-May

Menu 525/875 DKK (dinner only)

Chef:
Anita Klemensen and Lars Thomsen

Specialities:
Danish oysters with fennel, almond and horseradish. Poussin, creamy corn, chanterelles and pickled onions. Dark berries, toffee, brioche and sorrel.

An attractive former Forestry Officer's house dating back to 1881; built on the site of an old plantation. The small, romantic dining room is set with Royal Copenhagen porcelain and the lovely terrace offers partial sea views. The talented team offer monthly Nordic menus, informed by top seasonal produce.

DEN GULE COTTAGE ⅈ◯

DANISH • INN • MINIMALIST   𝒳 ≼ 🏠

Strandvejen 506 (North: 12 km by Folke Bernadottes Allé
and Road 2) ✉ 2930
TEL. 39 64 06 91 (booking advisable) – **www**.dengulecottage.dk
Closed 22 December-22 February and Monday-Tuesday
October-May

Menu 350 DKK – Carte 300/375 DKK

A lovely 1844 cottage facing the beach; from the same team as Den
Røde. Sit in one of two tiny, simply decorated rooms or on the large
terrace with its sea views. Choose from an unfussy menu of five main
dishes, salads and cheese plates.

SØLLERØD KRO ✿

MODERN CUISINE • INN   𝒳𝒳𝒳 ⊛ 🏠 ⇄ P

Søllerødvej 35 (North: 20 km by Nørre Allé) ✉ 2840
TEL. 45 80 25 05 – **www**.soelleroed-kro.dk
Closed 3 weeks July, 1 week February, Easter, Sunday dinner,
Monday and Tuesday

Menu 395/1095 DKK – Carte 930/1625 DKK

Specialities:
Organic Oscietra caviar with mussel
sauce. Black lobster, vin jaune and
morels à la crème. Gourmandise
desserts.

A characterful 17C thatched inn in a truly picturesque setting, with
three small but stylish dining rooms and a delightful courtyard terrace.
The superb wine list features plenty of burgundy and champagne.
Choose from an array of menus which offer classically based dishes
with deep, clear flavours.

HILTON COPENHAGEN AIRPORT

BUSINESS • LUXURY • MODERN

⟨ 🏂 ♿ 🖼 🆂🅿🅰 ♨ 🆎 🏊 🚗

Ellehammersvej 20 (Southeast: 10 km by Amager Boulevard) ✉ 2770
🅜 København Lufthavn
TEL. 32 50 15 01 – **www**.copenhagen.hilton.com

378 rm – 🧍 1395/3095 DKK 🧍🧍 1395/3095 DKK, 🍽 225 DKK – 5 suites

A smart, modern business hotel accessed from the airport via a
glass walkway. Spacious, well-maintained bedrooms have excellent
sound-proofing and offer good views from the higher floors. Relax
in the Asian-inspired Ni'mat Spa. Horizon offers everything from
sandwiches and grills to Nordic specialities.

AARHUS
Denmark

WeEm/Westend61 RM/age fotostock

Known as the world's smallest big city, Denmark's second city is a vibrant, versatile place, yet has the charm of a small town. It was originally founded by the Vikings in the 8th century and has been an important trading centre ever since. It's set on the Eastern edge of Jutland and is the country's main port; lush forests surround it, and there are beautiful beaches to the north and south. It's easy to enjoy the great outdoors, while also benefiting from the advantages of urban life. There's plenty to see and do, and most of it is within walking distance: the city centre is awash with shops – from big chains to quirky boutiques – as well as museums, bars and restaurants,

and the student population contributes to its youthful feel. The most buzzing area is Aboulevarden; a pedestrianized street which runs alongside the river, lined with clubs and cafés. Cultural activities are also high on the agenda of the European Capital of Culture 2017: visit the 12th century Cathedral and the ARoS Art Museum with its colourful rooftop panorama; witness the 2000 year old Grauballe man on display at the Moesgaard prehistoric museum; or step back in time at Den Gamle By. This is not a place that stands still and bold redevelopment projects are reshaping the cityscape, with shiny new apartment and office blocks springing up around the harbour.

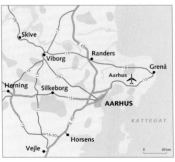

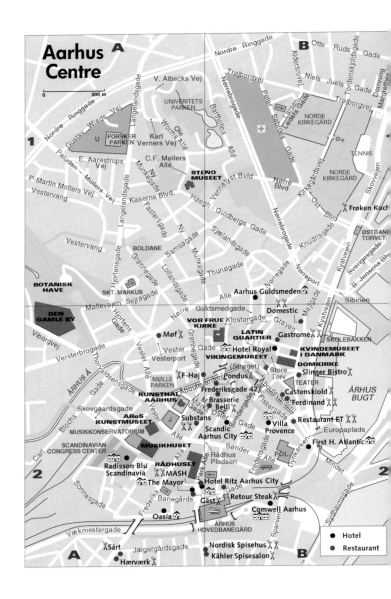

Aarhus A
Centre

0 ———— 300 m

Nordre Ringgade

V. Albecks Vej

Trøjborgvej

Nordre Ringgade

Gustav Wieds Vej

Langelandsgade

UNIVERITETS PARKEN

Bartholins Allé

Nørrebrogade

Peter Sabroes Gade

Larsen Leuns Gade

Trøjborgvej

B   Otte Ruds Gade
Aldersrovej
Niels Juels Gade
Tordenskjoldsgade
Dronning Margrethe...

NORDE KIRKEGÅRD

FORSKER PARKEN

U

Karl Verners Vej

Ole Worms Allé

E. Aarestrups Vej

Paludan - Müllers Vej

C.F. Møllers Allé

Ny Munkegade

STENO MUSEET

Nørre Blvd

TENNIS

Skovvejen

NORDE KIRKEGÅRD

Kirkegårdsvej

Øst Blvd

X Frøken Koch

P-Martin Mollers Vej

Vestervang

Kaserne Blvd.

Langelandsgade

Fastergade

Ny Munkegade

Høegh - Guldbergs Gade

Sjællandsgade

Nørrebrogade

Knudrisgade

ØSTBANI TORVET

Sverigesgade

B. Jensens Bl...

Vestervang

BOLDANE

Hjortensgade

Grønnegade

Samsøgade

Lollandsgade

Thunøgade

Nørregade

Nørreport

Kystvejen

Sibirien

BOTANISK HAVE

SKT. MARKUS

Mølllevejen

Sejrøgade

Allé

Aarhus Guldsmeden 🏨

DEN GAMLE BY

Hjortens Gade

Nørre

Guldsmedgade

Graven

Melbyse

Domestic

Viborgvej

Versterbrogade

Thorvaldsensgade

ÅRHUS Å

Vester Allé

VOR FRUE KIRKE

Klostergade

● Møf X

Grønnegade

Vester Vesterport

Gade

🏨 Hotel Royal ●

LATIN QUARTIER

Gastromé X X

SKOLEBAKKEN

KVINDEMUSEET I DANMARK

VIKINGEMUSEET

(Strøget)

Store Torv

DOMKIRKE

Slinger Bistro X

MØLLE PARKEN

X F-Høj

Pondus X

Abulle gården

TEATER

ÅRHUS BUGT

KUNSTHAL AARHUS

Mejlgade-Oster Gade

Frederiksgade 42 X

Brasserie Belli X

Castenskiold X

Ferdinand X X

Fiskergade

Skovgaardsgade

Blochs

ARoS KUNSTMUSEET

J

Substans ●

Sønder Gade

● Villa Provence

Restaurant ET X X

Europaplads

MUSIKKONSERVATORIUM

Allé

Scandic Aarhus City 🏨

First H. Atlantic 🏨

SCANDINAVIAN CONGRESS CENTER

MUSIKHUSET

Sønder

Park Allé

Rådhus Pladsen

POL.

Dynkarken

Mindet

Carl

Sonnesgade

Radisson Blu Scandinavia 🏨

RÅDHUSET

X X MASH

🏨 The Mayor

Fredensgade

Hotel Ritz Aarhus City 🏨

Sydhavnsgade

Frederiks Allé

Banegårds

Gade

Spanien

X Retour Steak X

Gäst X

Comwell Aarhus 🏨

Vækmestergade

Oasia 🏨

ÅRHUS HOVEDBANEGÅRD

X Sårt

Jægergårdsgade

Nordisk Spisehus X X

Kähler Spisesalon X

Hærværk X

● Hotel

● Restaurant

DOMESTIC ✿

DANISH • FASHIONABLE • MINIMALIST

Mejlgade 35B (through the arch) ✉ 8000 PLAN: B2
TEL. 61 43 70 10 – **www**.restaurantdomestic.dk
Closed Easter, 16-30 December, Sunday and Monday
Menu 500/900 DKK (dinner only) (tasting menu only)

Chef:
Morten Frølich Rastad and
Christoffer Norton

Specialities:
Fjord shrimps, green asparagus
and oyster. Beef with ramsons and
wild garlic. Apple and thyme.

The hottest ticket in town is this rustic yet elegant restaurant where 4
friends work together to serve skilfully cooked, feel-good food with
pure, natural flavours – using only Danish ingredients. Hanging hams,
pickling jars and cookbooks feature; menus offer 4 or 8 set courses;
fish dishes are a highlight.

FREDERIKSHØJ ✿

CREATIVE • ELEGANT • LUXURY

Oddervej 19 (South: 3.5 km by Spanien and Strandvejen) ✉ 8000
TEL. 86 14 22 80 (booking essential) – **www**.frederikshoj.com
Closed 4 weeks midsummer, 1 week October, Christmas-New Year
and Sunday-Tuesday
Menu 895 DKK (dinner only) (tasting menu only)

Chef:
Wassim Hallal

Specialities:
Tuna with caviar. Beef with carrot.
Strawberries and cream.

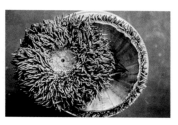

Set in the former staff lodge to the Royal Palace, this restaurant is
smart, luxurious and contemporary with edgy artwork, iPad menus
and floor to ceiling windows affording views over the gardens and out
to sea. Dishes are elaborate, creative and visually impressive. Service
is professional and knowledgeable.

GASTROMÉ ✿

MODERN CUISINE • FASHIONABLE • INTIMATE   XX ✛

Rosensgade 28 ✉ 8000 **PLAN: B2**
TEL. 28 78 16 17 – **www**.gastrome.dk
Closed 23 December-3 January, Sunday and Monday
Menu 548/848 DKK (dinner only) (tasting menu only)

Chef:
William Jørgensen
Specialities:
Monkfish, cauliflower, peas
and cocoa. Quail with morels
and broccoli. Summer berries,
elderflower and soured cream.

This intimate Latin Quarter restaurant features a semi open plan kitchen and stark white walls punctuated with contemporary art. The menu is divided in to a 'half throttle' of 4 courses and a 'full throttle' of 8, with wines to match. Complex cooking showcases modern techniques. Informative service.

SUBSTANS ✿

MODERN CUISINE • FRIENDLY • SIMPLE   XX ⒶⒸ

Frederiksgade 74 ✉ 8000 **PLAN: A2**
TEL. 86 23 04 01 – **www**.restaurantsubstans.dk
Closed Christmas, 28-30 July, Sunday-Tuesday
Menu 385/900 DKK (dinner only) (tasting menu only)

Chef:
René Mammen
Specialities:
Malt pie, clams and fermented
vegetables. Organic pork, carrots
and brown butter. Pickled apples,
thyme ice cream, caramel and dried
beans.

Classically Scandic in style, with a fresh, uncluttered feel, Pondus' older, more adventurous sister is run by the same experienced husband and wife team. Creative, contemporary cooking uses top quality, mostly organic, ingredients. Dishes have original touches, distinct flavours and stimulating combinations.

HÆRVÆRK 😊

DANISH • INTIMATE • FASHIONABLE

Frederiks Allé 105 ✉ 8000 PLAN: A2
TEL. 50 51 26 51 – **www**.restaurant-haervaerk.dk
Closed 2 weeks Christmas and 2 weeks summer
Menu 450 DKK (dinner only) (tasting menu only)

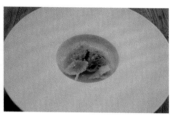

A lively place set in two converted shops; owned and run by four friends. Industrial-chic styling with a concrete floor, stark white décor and a glass-fronted fridge displaying hanging meats. Well-crafted Danish dishes with a rustic style and refined touch. Great value daily set menu; enthusiastic service.

PONDUS 😊

DANISH • BISTRO • RUSTIC

Åboulevarden 51 ✉ 8000 PLAN: B2
TEL. 28 77 18 50 (booking advisable) – **www**.restaurantpondus.dk
Closed Christmas, 1 week July, Sunday and Monday
Menu 295 DKK (dinner only)

Set by the narrow city centre canal, this little sister to Substans is a small, rustic bistro with a friendly vibe and a stripped back style. The blackboard menu offers great value, flavoursome cooking which uses organic Danish produce. Dishes are bright and colourful and represent great value.

BRASSERIE BELLI ⑩

CLASSIC FRENCH • BRASSERIE •
TRADITIONAL DÉCOR

X ⌂

Frederiksgade 54 ⊠ 8000 PLAN: B2
TEL. 86 12 07 60 – **www**.belli.dk
Closed 1 week July, Easter, Christmas and Sunday
Menu 240 DKK – Carte 340/460 DKK

An intimate, long-standing, family-owned restaurant on a
pedestrianised city centre street, offering satisfying, good value,
French brasserie classics and polite, friendly service. Check out the
owner's costumes from her circus days.

CASTENSKIOLD ⑩

MODERN CUISINE • FASHIONABLE • TRENDY   X ⌖ ⌂ A/C

Åboulevarden 32 ⊠ 8000 PLAN: B2
TEL. 86 18 90 90 – **www**.castenskiold.net
Closed Christmas, Easter and Sunday
Menu 350 DKK – Carte 365/450 DKK

Something a little different: set by the river on a busy pedestrianised
street, this trendy restaurant morphs into a bar and club as the day
goes on. Creative modern cooking relies on top quality produce and
the flavours shine through.

F-HØJ 🍴

SMØRREBRØD • NEIGHBOURHOOD • FRIENDLY   🍴 🏠

Grønnegade 2 ✉ 8000 PLAN: A2
TEL. (bookings not accepted) – **www**.fhoj.dk
Closed 4 weeks midsummer, Christmas-New Year,
Sunday and Monday
Menu 120 DKK – Carte 195/205 DKK (lunch only)

A bright, busy café with a pavement terrace; fridges and
cabinets display a tempting selection of desserts, cakes, biscuits and
drinks. Six choices of fresh, flavoursome classics on the smørrebrød
menu; two plus a light dessert should suffice.

FERDINAND 🍴

FRENCH • BRASSERIE • FASHIONABLE   XX 🐧 🏠 AC

Åboulevarden 28 ✉ 8000 PLAN: B2
TEL. 87 32 14 44 – **www**.hotelferdinand.dk
Closed 22 December-3 January
Menu 165/445 DKK – Carte 345/435 DKK

Red-canopied Ferdinand stands out from its neighbours on the
liveliest street in the city. Classic brasserie-style menus offer a mix of
French and Danish influenced dishes, with a great value set lunch and
small plates in the evening; a bar also serves tapas in the courtyard.
Bedrooms are comfy and spacious.

FREDERIKSGADE 42 ⅋◌

DANISH • NEIGHBOURHOOD • BISTRO   ✗

Frederiksgade 42 ✉ 8000 **PLAN: B2**
TEL. 60 68 96 06 – **www**.frederiksgade42.dk
Closed Sunday and Monday
Menu 198/398 DKK (dinner only) (tasting menu only)

The experienced owner extends a warm welcome to customers at this delightful restaurant in the heart of the city. The focus is on vegetarian dishes, with seasonal menus of well-priced small plates designed for sharing.

FRØKEN KOCH ⅋◌

DANISH • BISTRO • DESIGN   ✗ 🏠 AC

Kystpromenaden 5 ✉ 8000 **PLAN: B1**
TEL. 86 18 64 00 – **www**.kocherier.dk
Closed 22 December-4 January, Sunday and Monday
Menu 295 DKK – Carte 350/400 DKK

This bistro overlooks the marina, has a delightful raised terrace and is open all day for hearty, homely Danish classics which are full of flavour. Dishes like potato soup with smoked trout evoke memories of family meals in childhood.

GÄST ‌🍴

ITALIAN • BISTRO • FASHIONABLE   ✗ 🅿

The Mayor Hotel • Banegårdspladsen 14 ✉ 8000 PLAN: A2
TEL. 87 32 01 67 – **www**.gaest.dk
Closed 23 December-8 January

Menu 350 DKK – Carte 310/390 DKK

This spacious, relaxed Italian restaurant, set on the ground floor of
The Mayor Hotel, serves a seasonal, modern menu. Carefully cooked,
flavoursome dishes; everything is prepared in-house and pasta is
the highlight.

KÄHLER SPISESALON 🍴

SMØRREBRØD • NEIGHBOURHOOD •
TRADITIONAL DÉCOR   ✗ 🏠

M.P. Bruuns Gade 33 ✉ 8000 PLAN: A/B2
TEL. 86 12 20 53 (bookings not accepted) – **www**.spisesalon.dk
Closed 23-26 December and 1 January

Menu 200/360 DKK

An informal smørrebrød café, popular with shoppers and open in the
evening. They offer soups, salads, smørrebrød and pastries, as well as
organic juices and top-notch teas and coffees. Monochrome pictures
of Aarhus add to the charm.

CENTRE

MASH ⅃○

MEATS AND GRILLS • FASHIONABLE •
FRIENDLY

XX & ⌂ AC

Banegaardspladsen 12 ✉ 8000 **PLAN: A2**
TEL. 33 13 93 00 – **www**.mashsteak.dk
Closed 25-27 December and 1 January

Carte 280/1560 DKK

This Modern American Steak House (MASH) is bright and smart, with
colourful cow ornaments and red leather banquettes; sit in one of the
booths. Top quality imported USDA steak is listed alongside Danish
and even Japanese Kobe beef.

MØF ⅃○

DANISH • NEIGHBOURHOOD • TRENDY

X

Vesterport 10 ✉ 8000 **PLAN: A2**
TEL. 61 73 33 33 (booking essential) – **www**.restaurantmoef.com
Closed 23 December - 2 January, Tuesday and Wednesday

Menu 325 DKK – Carte 380/505 DKK (dinner only)

Owned and run by an experienced young couple, this restaurant
features monochrome décor and counter dining. There's a daily
3 course set menu and a concise à la carte; dishes are modern in style
but Danish at heart and made with local produce.

NORDISK SPISEHUS ⍢

MODERN CUISINE • NEIGHBOURHOOD •
FASHIONABLE   ✗✗ A/C

M.P.Bruuns Gade 31 ✉ 8000 PLAN: A/B2
TEL. 86 17 70 99 – **www**.nordiskspisehus.dk
Closed 23-26 December, 1 January and Sunday except December
Menu 500/800 DKK – Carte 240/545 DKK

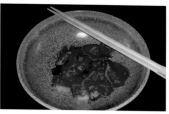

A smart, intimate restaurant with a unique concept: four themed
menus a year offering their own versions of dishes from Michelin
Starred restaurants around the globe. Décor changes along with the
theme: perhaps Japanese, Spanish or Nordic.

RESTAURANT ET ⍢

FRENCH • DESIGN • FASHIONABLE   ✗✗ 🕸 ⚹ 🏠 A/C ⇔

Åboulevarden 7 ✉ 8000 PLAN: B2
TEL. 86 13 88 00 – **www**.restaurant-et.dk
Closed Christmas and Sunday
Menu 358 DKK – Carte 374/514 DKK

You'll find charming service, modern brasserie styling and a central
kitchen at this well-run restaurant. Classic French dishes are full
of flavour; some come with a Danish twist. Superb wine choice,
particularly from France.

RETOUR STEAK ⁙○

MEATS AND GRILLS • FASHIONABLE • BISTRO

Banegårdspladsen 4 ✉ 8000 PLAN: B2
TEL. 88 63 02 90 – **www**.retoursteakaarhus.dk
Carte 265/490 DKK

A busy restaurant close to station: the latest outpost of the famed steak group. They serve some simple starters and puddings but the main focus is on meat, with tasty Danish rib-eye in various sizes accompanied by fluffy homemade chips.

SÅRT ⁙○

DANISH • TAPAS BAR • RUSTIC

Jægergårdsgade 6 ✉ 8000 PLAN: A2
TEL. 86 12 00 70 – **www**.saart.dk
Closed Sunday lunch and Monday
Menu 150/350 DKK – Carte 300/625 DKK

A simple but serious restaurant with its own deli: the first thing you see is a chiller filled with cured meats and preserved legs of ham; they also import whole cheeses, make their own pasta and have fresh bread delivered daily.

SLINGER BISTRO 🍴

DANISH • NEIGHBOURHOOD • FRIENDLY

Skolegade 5 ✉ 8000 PLAN: B2
TEL. 30 31 32 45 – www.slingerbistro.dk
Closed Christmas, 2 weeks in summer, Sunday and Wednesday
Menu 300 DKK – Carte 330/550 DKK (dinner only)

An intimate, personally run neighbourhood restaurant with homely
décor and an open kitchen at its heart. Modern, fiercely local cooking
on an à la carte and various set menus; 4 courses are sufficient. Good
selection of wines by the glass.

COMWELL AARHUS

BUSINESS • MODERN • DESIGN

Værkmestergade 2 ✉ 8000 PLAN: B2
TEL. 86 72 80 00 – www.comwellaarhus.dk
240 rm ☕ – 👤 998/1698 DKK 👥 1198/1898 DKK

A stylish, modern hotel set over 12 floors of a tower block. It's aimed
at businesspeople, with 19 meeting rooms; the largest with space for
475. Bedrooms are bright and contemporary with monsoon showers;
choose a corner Business Class room for super city views. Guest areas
include a bar and buzzy bistro.

CENTRE

RADISSON BLU SCANDINAVIA

BUSINESS • CHAIN • MODERN

Margrethepladsen 1 ⊠ 8000 PLAN: A2
TEL. 86 12 86 65 – www.radissonblu.com/hotel-aarhus
234 rm ☲ – ♦ 895/1890 DKK ♦♦ 895/1890 DKK – 5 suites

A conference-orientated hotel close to the ARoS Museum. Spacious, contemporary bedrooms offer all the facilities a modern traveller would expect. Business Class rooms and suites on the top two floors offer the best views along with extra touches. International dishes are served in the informal restaurant.

SCANDIC AARHUS CITY

BUSINESS • CHAIN • MODERN

Østergade 10 ⊠ 8000 PLAN: B2
TEL. 89 31 81 00 – www.scandichotels.com
228 rm ☲ – ♦ 895/1900 DKK ♦♦ 995/2700 DKK – 8 suites

Behind the 19C façade of a Viennese Renaissance café lies a smart, modern hotel with an open-plan lounge, lobby, bar and reception. Bright bedrooms feature photos of city scenes; suites have balconies. Solar panels supply electricity and rooftop hives provide honey. Grill restaurant with an open kitchen.

VILLA PROVENCE

TOWNHOUSE • TRADITIONAL • PERSONALISED

Fredens Torv 10-12 ✉ 8000 PLAN: B2
TEL. 86 18 24 00 – **www**.villaprovence.dk
Closed 22 December-2 January
39 rm ☕ – 👤 1295/1895 DKK 👥 1395/3000 DKK

Enter through an archway into a lovely cobbled terrace garden:
this charming and elegant townhouse is a little piece of Provence in
Aarhus. Proudly run by an amiable couple, it's furnished with French
antiques and features a traditional lounge full of books, and individual
bedrooms; some with four-posters.

FIRST H. ATLANTIC

BUSINESS • CHAIN • MODERN

Europaplads 10 ✉ 8000 PLAN: B2
TEL. 86 13 11 11 – **www**.firsthotels.dk
102 rm ☕ – 👤 995/1895 DKK 👥 1095/2195 DKK

Although its exterior can hardly be deemed charming, its rooms are
spacious and modern with good facilities, a balcony and a vista of
either the city or the sea. Breakfast with a view on the top floor.
Classic Italian dishes served in the smart restaurant. Gym membership
available at adjacent fitness club.

HOTEL RITZ AARHUS CITY

HISTORIC • TRADITIONAL • ART DÉCO

Banegårdspladsen 12 ✉ 8000 PLAN: A2
TEL. 86 13 44 44 – www.hotelritz.dk
Closed Christmas
67 rm ☜ – 👤 1045/1145 DKK 👥 1145/1245 DKK

An iconic 1932 hotel in distinctive yellow brick, situated opposite the railway station. Friendly and welcoming with an appealing art deco style and neatly refurbished, modern bedrooms in warm colours. Showers only in most rooms.

HOTEL ROYAL

HISTORIC • TRADITIONAL • CLASSIC

Store Torv 4 ✉ 8000 PLAN: B2
TEL. 86 12 00 11 – www.hotelroyal.dk
63 rm – 👤 995/1895 DKK 👥 1195/2045 DKK, ☜ 95 DKK – 5 suites

Beside the cathedral is the city's oldest hotel; open for around 175 years and with a wonderfully classic feel – enhanced by paintings depicting the Kings and Queens of Denmark. Very spacious bedrooms combine antique furniture and modern facilities. The informal restaurant serves international dishes.

THE MAYOR

FAMILY • TOWNHOUSE • MODERN

Banegårdspladsen 14 ✉ 8000 PLAN: A2
TEL. 87 32 01 00 – **www**.themayor.dk
Closed 23 December-8 January
162 rm ⌂ – ♦ 795/1995 DKK ♦♦ 1045/2095 DKK
GÄST – See restaurant listing

Recently refurbished in a contemporary style, this hotel is situated close to the train station and has been owned by the same family for over twenty years. Cosy bedrooms have a modern industrial feel.

AARHUS GULDSMEDEN

TOWNHOUSE • TRADITIONAL • PERSONALISED

Guldsmedgade 40 ✉ 8000 PLAN: B1
TEL. 86 13 45 50 – **www**.guldsmedenhotels.com
Closed 30 December-2 January
22 rm ⌂ – ♦ 945/1325 DKK ♦♦ 1075/1575 DKK

A relaxed hotel with an eco/organic ethos and a friendly atmosphere. Simply decorated bedrooms vary in shape and size; some feature antique furniture and the larger rooms have four posters. Complimentary tea, coffee and juice.

OASIA

TOWNHOUSE • TRADITIONAL • DESIGN

Kriegersvej 27-31 ⊠ 8000 PLAN: A2
TEL. 87 32 37 15 – **www**.hoteloasia.com
Closed 24-25 December

65 rm ♨ – ♦ 895/1595 DKK ♦♦ 895/1795 DKK

After a day's sightseeing or shopping, you will be happy to head back to this hotel in a quieter area of the city. Bright, uncluttered bedrooms offer good facilities; go for one of the suites with their modern four posters.

KADEAU ✿

CREATIVE • MINIMALIST 🗙 ⪕ ♨ **P**

Baunevej 18, Vestre Sømark Pedersker, Åkirkeby (Southeast: 23 km by 38) ✉ 3720
TEL. 56 97 82 50 (booking essential) – **www**.kadeau.dk
Closed mid September-late April

Menu 800/1200 DKK (dinner only and lunch in July-August)
(tasting menu only)

Chef:
Nicolai Nørregaard
Specialities:
Blue mussels, fermented wheat and elderberries. Hay-smoked celeriac, wild onion buds and burnt cheese. Caramelised buttermilk tart.

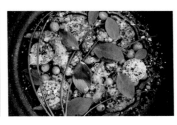

A remote beachside eatery with a superb sea panorama, which is best enjoyed from its terrace, although all tables have the view. The atmosphere is relaxed but they are serious about food here and the set no-choice menu of 5 or 8 dishes offers accomplished, original cooking with superbly balanced, contrasting flavours.

LASSEN'S 🍴

MODERN CUISINE • CONTEMPORARY DÉCOR 🗙🗙 ✾ ⪕ 🛋 **P**

Stammershalle Badehotel • Sdr. Strandvej 128, Stammershalle, Gudhjem (Northeast: 24 km by 159 on 158) ✉ 3760
TEL. 56 48 42 10 (booking essential) – **www**.stammershalle-badehotel.dk
Closed January-February and mid week in winter

Menu 450/595 DKK (dinner only) (tasting menu only)

A light and airy New England style restaurant in a charming coastal hotel, with stunning sea views. Seasonal island ingredients are prepared with skill and passion by the young kitchen and the modern dishes have distinct flavours and interesting combinations. Set 3 and 5 course menus. Engaging service.

STAMMERSHALLE BADEHOTEL

LUXURY • SEASIDE

⬅ 🛏 ⚒ 🎾 🚣 🚴 🏊 **P**

Sdr. Strandvej 128, Stammershalle, Gudhjem (Northeast: 24 km by 159 on 158) ✉ 3760
TEL. 56 48 42 10 – **www**.stammershalle-badehotel.dk
Closed mid November-Easter
15 rm ⬚ – 🧍 700 DKK 🧍🧍 900/1500 DKK
LASSEN'S – See restaurant listing

This cosy hotel opened in 1911 and is run with a passion. Stylish whilst also respecting tradition, it is situated in an enviable position and boasts superb sea views, as well as the opportunity to go bathing in the Baltic just across the road. Bedrooms offer straightforward comforts and a simple Scandinavian style.

MOLSKROEN 🍽

MODERN CUISINE •
CONTEMPORARY DÉCOR • DESIGN   XX ⬅ 🛏 🏠 ⬚ **P**

Molskroen Hotel • Hovedgaden 16, Femmøller Strand (Northwest: 7 km by 21) ✉ 8400
TEL. 86 36 22 00 (booking essential) – **www**.molskroen.dk
Closed Sunday, Monday-Tuesday mid January-mid March and lunch September-mid March
Menu 450/850 DKK

A stylish, relaxed and well-regarded seaside inn with a reputation for gastronomy; a table on the charming terrace is the perfect spot to enjoy traditional French cuisine as well as more modern interpretations of the classics.

MOLSKROEN

INN • LUXURY • CONTEMPORARY

⟨ 🛏 🏠 ⛵ 🅿

Hovedgaden 16, Femmøller Strand (Northwest: 7 km by 21) ✉ 8400
TEL. 86 36 22 00 – **www**.molskroen.dk
Closed 1-13 January

8 rm – 🛏 950/1280 DKK 👫 1280/1680 DKK – 10 suites ⚏ –
🛏 2100/3500 DKK 👫 2100/3500 DKK
MOLSKROEN – See restaurant listing

This inn, located in Mols Bjerge National Park, was built by renowned
architect Egil Fischer in 1923 and over the years it has gained a
considerable reputation. The traditional timbered façade contrasts
with its stylish, modern interior.

KOKS ✿

CREATIVE • CONTEMPORARY DÉCOR • INTIMATE   XX ⟨

Í Geilini 13, Tórshavn (South: 11 Km by 12) ✉ 175
TEL. 333 999 (booking essential) – **www**.koks.fo
Closed December-mid April and Sunday

Menu 1085 DKK (dinner only) (tasting menu only)

Specialities:
Langoustine and pine. Lamb's head
and potatoes. Lemon verbena and
thyme.

Located in a remote coastal hamlet, with stunning view over the fjords.
The chef comes from the island – as do the excellent ingredients –
and the kitchen uses both modern and more traditional techniques
like drying, fermenting, smoking and salting to create accomplished,
imaginative, intensely flavoured dishes.

TI TRIN NED ✿

MODERN • INTIMATE • HISTORIC ✕✕✕

Norgesgade 3 ✉ 7000
TEL. 75 93 33 55 (booking essential) – **www**.titrinned.dk
Closed 9 July-5 August, Sunday and Monday
Menu 685/1085 DKK (dinner only)

Chef:
Rainer Gassner

Specialities:
Fried scallop with sweet peas and blackcurrants. Organic pork with truffle-smoked sauce. White chocolate crème, green apple sorbet.

Run by an experienced couple; its name meaning 'ten steps down', which is exactly the number you take from the pretty rear courtyard down to the vaulted cellar of this 19C building. Founded on produce from their own garden, cooking is original yet understated; well-balanced and full of flavour. Formal service.

HENNE KIRKEBY KRO ✿✿

CLASSIC CUISINE • INN • FRIENDLY ✕✕✕ 🌳 🍴 ♿ 🅿

Strandvejen 234 ✉ 6854
TEL. 75 25 54 00 (booking essential) – **www**.hennekirkebykro.dk
Closed 3 December-23 March, Wednesday lunch and Sunday-Tuesday
Menu 495/1150 DKK – Carte lunch 635/715 DKK

Chef:
Paul Cunningham

Specialities:
Langoustine, smoked butter bisque and tomato confit. Fallow deer with beetroot and plum. Italian citrus fruits and meringue.

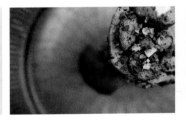

A charming 18C thatched inn with a contrastingly modern interior. Menus celebrate the surrounding farmland, with top-notch seasonal produce including plenty from their own kitchen garden. Cooking is founded on the classics and dishes are original and technically accomplished; sauces are sublime. Attentive, very personable service; luxurious, super-stylish bedrooms.

BRYGHUSET VENDIA - GOURMET ⅋◐

CREATIVE • INTIMATE •
CONTEMPORARY DÉCOR ✗✗ A|C P

Markedsgade 9 ✉ 9800
TEL. 98 92 22 29 (booking essential) – **www**.bryghusetvendia.dk
Closed 2 weeks July, 29-31 December and Sunday-Wednesday

Menu 2000 DKK (dinner only) (surprise menu only)

A microbrewery with a stylish brasserie and a tiny gourmet restaurant.
The latter consists of just three tables and serves an 11 course themed
surprise menu of creative, elaborately presented dishes, designed to
stimulate the senses.

SLOTSSKØKKENET ❁

CREATIVE • INTIMATE • FRIENDLY ✗✗✗ 🍷 P

Dragsholm Slot Hotel • Dragsholm Allé
(Northwest: 6.5 km by 231 on 225) ✉ 4534
TEL. 59 65 33 00 (booking essential) – **www**.dragsholm-slot.dk
Closed Sunday and Monday and restricted opening November-mid
April

Menu 700/900 DKK (dinner only) (tasting menu only)

Specialities:
Langoustine with sunflower seeds
and red berries. Sweetbreads,
blackcurrant and blood sauce.
Candied herbs with sheeps'
yoghurt and celery sorbet.

This atmospheric cellar restaurant is set in the former kitchens of an
impressive 800 year old castle. Innovative, accomplished, intensely
flavoured cooking has herbs and vegetables from the country's most
fertile region at its core – many foraged by the head chef. A 5 or 7
course menu satisfies all the senses.

DRAGSHOLM SLOT

HISTORIC BUILDING • GRAND LUXURY

< 🌒 🛏 👁 🚴 **P**

Dragsholm Allé (Northwest: 6.5 km by 231 on 225) ✉ 4534
TEL. 59 65 33 00 – **www**.dragsholm-slot.dk

36 rm ☐ – 🛉 2095 DKK 🛉🛉 4050 DKK

SLOTSSKØKKENET ✿ – See restaurant listing

A charming 800 year old fortified manor house with beautiful grounds
and a moat; one of the oldest secular buildings in Denmark. The
interior is modern yet full of character, with luxurious, classically
decorated bedrooms featuring antique furniture and four-poster
beds. Dine in the relaxed bistro, Spisehuset, or enjoy a gastronomic
experience in Slotskøkkenet.

SLETTEN 🍴

MODERN CUISINE • FASHIONABLE • BISTRO

🍴 🍸 < 🏠 🖵

Gl Strandvej 137 ✉ 3050
TEL. 49 19 13 21 (booking essential) – **www**.sletten.dk
Closed Sunday and Monday in winter
Menu 750 DKK (dinner) – Carte 390/440 DKK

A relaxed former inn in a charming coastal village; most people head
to the room with the sea view, although the others with their bold
foodie pictures are equally as pleasant. Well-presented, modern small
plates make up the menu; about 2 or 3 per person is sufficient.
Interesting wine list.

FRU LARSEN ⅋○

MODERN CUISINE • RUSTIC • COSY   XX 🅿

Fru Larsen Hotel • Østergade 1, Laurbjerg (South: 6.5 km on 587) ✉ 8870
TEL. 86 46 83 88 – **www**.frularsen.dk
Closed 16 July-4 August and 17 December-5 January, Sunday and Monday
Menu 420/599 DKK – Carte 450/620 DKK

A long-standing, simply furnished and cosy hotel restaurant with a wood-panelled ceiling and a fire burning in the hearth. Lighter dishes at lunch; set 5 course dinner menu. Dishes are well-presented, carefully crafted and full of flavour.

FRU LARSEN   🏠

TRADITIONAL • COSY
🏹 🛋 🅿

Østergade 1, Laurbjerg (South: 6.5 km on 587) ✉ 8870
TEL. 86 46 83 88 – **www**.frularsen.dk
Closed 16 July-4 August and 17 December-5 January
16 rm ☕ – 🛉 899 DKK 🛉🛉 1149 DKK
FRU LARSEN – See restaurant listing

Set on the main road through this small town. Spacious, wood-floored bedrooms; half are decorated in a traditional, fire-lit 'romantic' style; half have a more modern, minimalistic feel and either a Parisian, Colonial or Antipodean theme.

FALSLED KRO ⚑🍴

CLASSIC CUISINE • ELEGANT •
COUNTRY HOUSE

XxX 🛏 🅿

Falsled Kro Hotel • Assensvej 513 ✉ 5642
TEL. 62 68 11 11 (bookings essential for non-residents) –
www.falsledkro.dk
Closed 17 December-4 January, Sunday and Monday September-
May and Thursday January-May
Menu 545/850 DKK (tasting menu only)

A formal hotel dining room; rustic and beamed, with a vast feature
fireplace, an open kitchen and an extension overlooking the garden.
Set 3, 6 or 10 course menus offer accomplished, classically based
dishes with bold flavours and modern touches. Ingredients are top-
notch and service, detailed and professional.

FALSLED KRO

INN • HISTORIC • ELEGANT
🛏 ⚐ ♿ 🅿

Assensvej 513 ✉ 5642
TEL. 62 68 11 11 - **www**.falsledkro.dk
Closed 17 December-4 January
19 rm – ♦ 2900 DKK ♦♦ 3400 DKK, ☕ 275 DKK – 9 suites
FALSLED KRO – See restaurant listing

In a small village off the beaten track is this professionally run, historic
inn with a hugely characterful interior boasting flagged floors,
wooden beams and a pretty central courtyard. Some bedrooms are
in the original building; others are in the charming period cottages
across the road in the lovely gardens.

PASFALL ⁜◐

MODERN CUISINE • FASHIONABLE • DESIGN ⅩⅩ A/C

Brandts Passage 31 ⊠ 5000
TEL. 23 27 00 00 – **www**.thomaspasfall.dk
Closed 16 July-7 August, 23 December-4 January, Sunday and Monday
Menu 345/595 DKK

Watch the eponymous chef at work in the open kitchen of this bright, contemporary restaurant. Top seasonal ingredients are used to create robustly flavoured dishes which are classic in their foundation but modern in delivery.

FREDERIKSMINDE ✿

CREATIVE • ELEGANT • INTIMATE ⅩⅩ ← ⌂ ⌖ P

Hotel Frederiksminde • Klosternakken 9 ⊠ 4720
TEL. 55 90 90 30 (booking essential) – **www**.frederiksminde.com
Closed 23-26 December, 1-16 January, Sunday-Monday and lunch Tuesday-Thursday in September-May
Menu 450/1195 DKK (tasting menu only)

Chef:
Jonas Mikkelsen

Specialities:
Salted halibut with leeks and mussel juice. Dry-aged beef with wild mushrooms and fermented celeriac. Rose hip sorbet with salted honey.

A spacious and airy hotel summer room with only 8 tables and an aspect that takes in the garden and the fjord. Creative modern cooking uses superb seasonal ingredients in original yet well-judged combinations. Dishes are precisely crafted and attractively presented and service is knowledgeable and professional.

FREDERIKSMINDE

COUNTRY HOUSE • ELEGANT • CLASSIC

Klosternakken 8 ✉ 4720
TEL. 55 90 90 30 – www.frederiksminde.com
Closed 23-26 December and 1-16 January
19 rm 🛏 – 🛉 1145 DKK 🛉🛉 1545 DKK
FREDERIKSMINDE ❀ – See restaurant listing

An attractive 19C house named after a former king of Denmark; it has
a classic, understated style and offers superb views. Bedrooms are
tastefully furnished, well-kept and comfortable; antiques and fine
portraits feature.

RUTHS GOURMET RESTAURANT 🍴

CREATIVE • FASHIONABLE

Ruths Hotel • Hans Ruth Vej 1 ✉ 9990
TEL. 98 44 11 24 (booking essential) – www.ruths-hotel.dk
Closed 2 weeks January, Sunday-Thursday except Tuesday-
Wednesday July-August and Thursday May-June and September
Menu 595 DKK (dinner only) (tasting menu only)

Situated in a seaside hotel in Denmark's most northerly town. Set 3,
4, 5 or 8 course menus of creative, elaborate modern cooking. The
meal starts with a personal introduction from the chef. Opening times
change throughout the year.

RUTHS

HOLIDAY HOTEL • CONTEMPORARY

Hans Ruth Vej 1 ✉ 9990
TEL. 98 44 11 24 - www.ruths-hotel.dk
Closed 2 weeks in January
52 rm ☕ - 🚹 1750/2050 DKK 🚻 1750/2050 DKK - 5 suites
RUTHS GOURMET RESTAURANT - See restaurant listing

A long-standing seaside hotel, where families are made to feel particularly welcome. Bedrooms are spread over a number of adjoining properties and are bright, comfortable and up-to-date. Enjoy creative, modern cooking in Ruths Gourmet Restaurant or bistro classics in the relaxed French Brasserie.

THE RESTAURANT BY KROUN

MODERN CUISINE • DESIGN • INTIMATE

A/C P

Kurhotel Skodsborg • Skodsborg Strandvej 139 ✉ 2942
TEL. 27 90 28 64 (booking essential) - www.skodsborg.dk
Closed Sunday-Wednesday
Menu 700/900 DKK (dinner only) (tasting menu only)

A stylish, formal restaurant on the ground floor of a grand Victorian spa hotel; each of the seven tables has a view across the water. Tasting menus feature creative, elaborate, modern dishes. Professional service; popular chef's table.

KURHOTEL SKODSBORG

LUXURY • SPA AND WELLNESS • CONTEMPORARY

Skodsborg Strandvej 139 ✉ 2942
TEL. 45 58 58 00 – **www.skodsborg.dk**
83 rm ☐ – 🛉 1100/1300 DKK 🛉🛉 1700/4000 DKK – 2 suites
THE RESTAURANT BY KROUN – See restaurant listing

A grand hotel with a world-renowned spa; founded in 1898 and
recently rejuvenated by a substantial facelift. Luxury bedrooms have
a modern style; choose one with a balcony to make the most of the
view across the Oresund Strait. Enjoy a cocktail on the rooftop terrace
or a relaxed meal in the third floor brasserie.

TREE TOP 🍴

MODERN CUISINE • CLASSIC DÉCOR

På Munkebjerg Hotel, Munkebjergvej 125
(East: 8.75 km by 24) ✉ 7100
TEL. 76 42 85 00 (booking essential) – **www.tree-top.dk**
Closed July and 21 December-3 January
Menu 495/1500 DKK (dinner only) (tasting menu only)

Smart, light-filled hotel restaurant with an impressive view over the
tree tops and the Vejle Fjord. Enjoy an aperitif in the cellars while you
choose 3, 5 or 7 courses (or the surprise 12 course menu); dishes are
modern, elaborate and original.

Ch. Boisvieux/hemis.fr

FINLAND

AWARDS

HELSINKI

Finland

J. Arnold Images/hemis.fr

Cool, clean and chic, the 'Daughter of the Baltic' sits prettily on a peninsula, jutting out between the landmasses of its historical overlords, Sweden and Russia. Surrounded on three sides by water, Helsinki is a busy port, but that only tells a small part of the story: forests grow in abundance around here and trees reach down to the lapping shores. This is a striking city to look at: it was rebuilt in the 19C after a fire, and many of the buildings have a handsome neoclassical or art nouveau façade. Shoppers can browse the picturesque

outdoor food and tourist markets stretching along the main harbour, where island-hopping ferries ply their trade. In a country with over 200,000 lakes it would be pretty hard to escape a green sensibility, and the Finnish capital has made sure that concrete and stone have never taken priority over its distinctive features of trees, water and open space. There are bridges at every turn connecting the city's varied array of small islands, and a ten kilometre strip of parkland acts as a spine running vertically up from the centre. Renowned as a city of cool, it's somewhere that also revels in a hot nightlife and even hotter saunas – this is where they were invented. And if your blast of dry heat has left you wanting a refreshing dip, there's always a freezing lake close at hand.

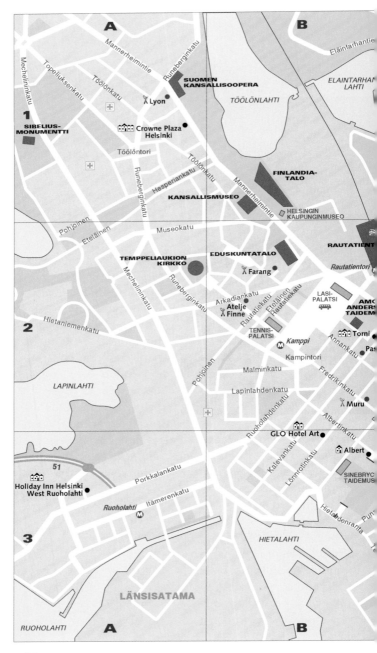

A

Mannerheimintie

Runeberginkatu

Mecheliininkatu

Topeliuksenkatu

Töölönkatu

X Lyon

SUOMEN
KANSALLISOOPERA

B

Eläintarhantie

ELAINTARHAN
LAHTI

TÖÖLÖNLAHTI

1

SIBELIUS-
MONUMENTTI

Crowne Plaza
Helsinki

Töölöntori

Runeberginkatu

Töölönkatu

Hesperiankatu

Mannerheimintie

FINLANDIA-
TALO

KANSALLISMUSEO

HELSINGIN
KAUPUNGINMUSEO

Pohjoinen

Eteläinen

Museokatu

RAUTATIEN

TEMPPELIAUKION
KIRKKO

EDUSKUNTATALO

X Farang

Rautatientori

Mecheliininkatu

Runeberginkatu

Arkadiankatu

Atelje
X Finne

Rautatiekatu

Eteläinen
Rautatiekatu

LASI-
PALATSI

AMO
ANDERS
TAIDEM

2

Hietaniemenkatu

Pohjoinen

TENNIS-
PALATSI

Kamppi

Annankatu

Torni

Pas

Kampintori

Malminkatu

Fredrikinkatu

LAPINLAHTI

Lapinlahdenkatu

X Muru

Ruoholahdenkatu

Albertinkatu

GLO Hotel Art

Kalevankatu

Lönnrotinkatu

Albert

SINEBRYC
TAIDEMUS

51

Holiday Inn Helsinki
West Ruoholahti

Porkkalankatu

Ruoholahti

Itämerenkatu

Hietalahdenranta

Pun

3

HIETALAHTI

LÄNSISATAMA

RUOHOLAHTI

A

B

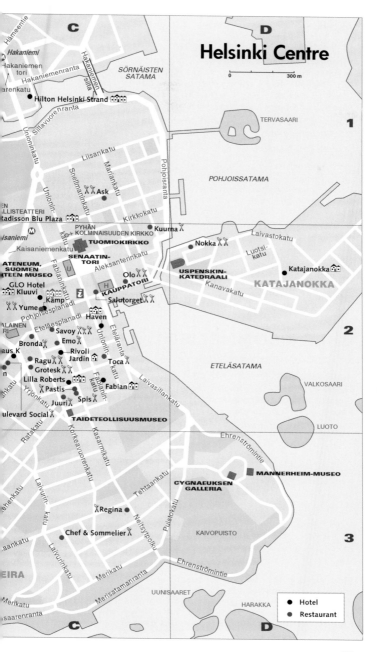

Helsinki Centre

0   300 m

C
D

Hameentie
Hakaniemi
Hakaniemen tori
Hakaniemenranta
arenkatu
Hakaniemen silta
SÖRNÄISTEN SATAMA

● Hilton Helsinki Strand

TERVASAARI

1

Siltavuorenranta

Liisankatu

Unioninkatu

Snellmaninkatu

Mariankatu

Pohjoisranta

POHJOISSATAMA

Kirkkokatu

X X Ask

EN LLISTEATTERI
Radisson Blu Plaza

PYHÄN KOLMINAISUUDEN KIRKKO

● Kuurna X

isaniemi
Kaisaniemenkatu
M
Kaisaniemenkatu

Unioninkatu
Kol...katu

TUOMIOKIRKKO
SENAATIN-TORI

Laivastokatu

● Nokka X X

Luotsi-katu

ATENEUM, SUOMEN TEEN MUSEO
U
Aleksanterinkatu

Fabianinkatu

Olo X X

Katajanokka ●

USPENSKIN-KATEDRAALI

KATAJANOKKA

GLO Hotel
Kluuvi
X X Yume
● Kämp

i
Pohjoisesplanadi

KAUPPATORI
H
Salutorget X X

Kanavakatu

ALAINEN
Ri

Etelaesplanadi

Haven

Savoy X X X

Bronda X
● Emo X

Unioninkatu

 aus K
Ragu X X
● Rivoli
Jardin
Toca X

Eteläranta

ETELÄSATAMA

VALKOSAARI

Grotesk X X
Lilla Roberts
X Pastis
Juuri X
Spis X

Fabianinkatu

Fabian

Laivasillankatu

LUOTO

Yrjönkatu

ulevard Social X

TAIDETEOLLISUUSMUSEO

Ratakatu

Korkeavuorenkatu

Kasarmikatu

Ehrenströmintie

MANNERHEIM-MUSEO

CYGNAEUKSEN GALLERIA

ehenkatu

Lavurin katu

Tehtaankatu

Puistokatu

X Regina ●

● Chef & Sommelier X

KAIVOPUISTO

3

aankatu

Laivurinkatu

Neitsytpolku

Merikatu

Ehrenströmintie

EIRA

Merikatu

Merisatamanranta

UUNISAARET

saarenranta

HARAKKA

C
D

●	Hotel
●	Restaurant

95

CENTRE

ASK ✿

MODERN CUISINE • INTIMATE

Vironkatu 8 ⊠ 00170 **PLAN: C1**
Ⓜ Kaisaniemi
TEL. 040 5818100 – **www**.restaurantask.com
Closed 3 weeks in July, Easter, Christmas, Sunday,
Monday and bank holidays
Menu 49/98€ (dinner only and lunch Friday-Saturday)
(tasting menu only)

Chef:
Filip Langhoff
Specialities:
Reindeer and hazelnut. Pike-perch
with parsnip. White chocolate and
sorrel.

It may be hidden away but this welcoming restaurant is well-known.
It's a charming place, run by a delightful, experienced couple, who
offer modern Nordic cooking crafted almost entirely from organic
ingredients. Dishes are light and original, produce is top quality and
flavours are clearly defined.

CHEF & SOMMELIER ✿

MODERN CUISINE • NEIGHBOURHOOD

Huvilakatu 28 ⊠ 00150 **PLAN: C3**
TEL. 040 0959440 (booking essential) – **www**.chefetsommelier.fi
Closed late June-early August, 10 days Christmas-New Year, 1 week
February, Easter, Sunday and Monday
Menu 46/76€ (dinner only) (tasting menu only)

Chef:
Sasu Laukkonen
Specialities:
River Teno salmon with summer
greens. Lamb with mushrooms and
roots. Blueberry and pine.

Tiny, simply decorated restaurant with a friendly atmosphere,
secreted amongst residential apartment blocks. The open kitchen
uses carefully chosen organic and wild ingredients in modern, original
Finnish cooking. The passionate chefs deliver dishes to the tables
themselves and explain the techniques used.

DEMO ⌘

MODERN CUISINE • INTIMATE

XX ⌐

Uudenmaankatu 9-11 ✉ 00120 PLAN: C2
Ⓜ Rautatientori
TEL. 09 22890840 (booking essential) – www.restaurantdemo.fi
Closed 4 weeks in July-August, Christmas-New Year, Easter, midsummer, Sunday and Monday
Menu 62/102€ (dinner only) (tasting menu only)

Chef:
Tommi Tuominen

Specialities:
Fermented pea soup with pancetta and sour cream. Sautéed pike with cabbage and oat miso. Cloudberry mousse with brown butter ice cream.

An unassuming-looking restaurant decorated in neutral tones and hung with huge cotton pendant lights. Classically based cooking combines French and Finnish influences to produce robust, satisfying dishes with a subtle modern edge. Choose 4-7 courses; the menu is presented verbally and changes almost daily.

OLO ⌘

MODERN CUISINE • DESIGN • CONTEMPORARY DÉCOR

XX ⌐ Ⓐ⌐ ⌐ ⌐

Pohjoisesplanadi 5 ✉ 00170 PLAN: C2
Ⓜ Kaisaneimi
TEL. 010 3206250 (booking essential) – www.olo-ravintola.fi
Closed Easter, midsummer, Christmas, Saturday lunch, Sunday and Monday
Menu 52/139€ (tasting menu only)

Chef:
Jari Vesivalo

Specialities:
Chicken liver with gooseberries. Finnish lamb with onion. Rhubarb and sour milk.

A modern, minimalist restaurant set within an attractive harbourside townhouse. Exciting, innovative cooking features stimulating ingredient combinations with contrasting textures and tastes. At dinner choose 'The Journey' or the 'The Shorter Way'; alternatively book a table in the Creative Kitchen to interact with the chefs and try out their latest creations.

BOULEVARD SOCIAL 😊

MEDITERRANEAN CUISINE • FASHIONABLE

Bulevardi 6 ⊠ 00120 PLAN: C2
Ⓜ Rautatientori
TEL. 010 3229382 – **www**.boulevardsocial.fi
Closed Christmas, midsummer, Saturday lunch and Sunday
Menu 29€ (lunch) – Carte 26/50€

Owned by the same people as next door Gaijin, this lively, informal
restaurant offers an accessible range of authentic North African,
Turkish and Eastern Mediterranean dishes; try the set or tasting menus
to experience a cross-section of them all. If they're fully booked, ask
for a seat at the counter.

EMO 😊

MODERN CUISINE • FASHIONABLE

Kasarmikatu 44 ⊠ 00130 PLAN: C2
Ⓜ Rautatientori
TEL. 010 5050900 – **www**.emo-ravintola.fi
Closed Christmas, Sunday, lunch Saturday and Monday
Menu 27/63€ – Carte 34/56€

Laid-back restaurant with an adjoining bar and a friendly team.
The menu is easy-going too, offering around 10 regularly changing
dishes that can be taken either as starters or main courses. Quality
ingredients feature in flavoursome, unfussy preparations, which are
good value and come with a contemporary touch.

FARANG 🍴

SOUTH EAST ASIAN • SIMPLE • INTIMATE

Ainonkatu 3 (inside the Kunsthalle) ✉ 00100 PLAN: B2
Ⓜ Kamppi
TEL. 010 3229380 – www.farang.fi
Closed Christmas, midsummer, Easter, Saturday lunch, Sunday and
Monday
Menu 29€ (lunch) – Carte 38/44€

This stylish, modern restaurant is housed in the Kunsthalle art centre.
One room is decorated with large photos of Thai scenes and has
communal tables; the other is more intimate and furnished in red,
black and grey. Zesty, harmonious dishes take their influences from
Vietnam, Thailand and Malaysia.

GAIJIN 🍴

ASIAN • FASHIONABLE

Bulevardi 6 ✉ 00120 PLAN: C2
Ⓜ Rautatientori
TEL. 010 3229381 (booking essential) – www.gaijin.fi
Closed Christmas, midsummer and lunch Saturday-Monday
Menu 37€ (lunch) – Carte 39/50€

Gaijin comes with dark, contemporary décor, a buzzing atmosphere,
attentive service and an emphasis on sharing. Its experienced owners
offer boldly flavoured, skilfully presented modern takes on Japanese,
Korean and Northern Chinese recipes. The tasting menus are a great
way to sample the different cuisines.

ATELJÉ FINNE 🍴

MODERN CUISINE • BISTRO

Arkadiankatu 14 ✉ 00100 PLAN: B2
Ⓜ Kamppi
TEL. 010 2828242 (booking advisable) – **www**.ateljefinne.fi
Closed Christmas, Easter, midsummer, weekends in July, Sunday
and Monday
Menu 42€ – Carte 42/61€ (dinner only)

This is the old studio of Finnish sculptor Gunnar Finne, who worked
here for over 30 years. Local art decorates the small bistro-style
dining rooms on three levels. Regional dishes are given subtle modern
and international twists.

BRONDA 🍴

MODERN CUISINE • FASHIONABLE • BRASSERIE

Eteläesplanadi 20 ✉ 00130 PLAN: C2
Ⓜ Rautatientori
TEL. 010 3229383 – **www**.ravintolabronda.fi
Closed Christmas, midsummer and Sunday
Menu 29/57€ – Carte 38/70€

The floor to ceiling windows of this old furniture showroom flood it
with light. Have cocktails and snacks at the bar or comforting, boldly
flavoured, Mediterranean sharing plates in the brasserie. Each dish
arrives as it's ready.

GROTESK ⁝○

MEATS AND GRILLS • FASHIONABLE •
BRASSERIE   ✗✗ 🏠 AC ⥮ ⟳

Ludviginkatu 10 ✉ 00130 PLAN: C2
Ⓜ Rautatientori
TEL. 010 4702100 – **www**.grotesk.fi
Closed Easter, Christmas, midsummer, Sunday and Monday
Menu 49€ – Carte 39/79€ (dinner only)

Smart, buzzy restaurant behind an impressive 19C façade;
which comprises a fashionable cocktail bar, a wine bar serving
interesting small plates, and a chic dining room decorated in black,
white and red, that specialises in steaks.

JUURI ⁝○

TRADITIONAL CUISINE • BISTRO   ✗ ⥮

Korkeavuorenkatu 27 ✉ 00130 PLAN: C2
TEL. 09 635732 – **www**.juuri.fi
Closed midsummer and 24-26 December
Carte 36/53€

A small bistro close to the Design Museum, with friendly service and a
rustic style. Menus offer a few main dishes along with 'Sapas' – small,
tapas-style plates of organic produce. Traditional Finnish recipes are
brought up-to-date.

KUURNA ⫶○

TRADITIONAL CUISINE • NEIGHBOURHOOD

Meritullinkatu 6 ⊠ 00170 **PLAN: C2**
Ⓜ Kaisaniemi
TEL. 010 2818241 (booking essential) – **www**.kuurna.fi
Closed 10 days Christmas, Good Friday and Sunday
Menu 44€ (dinner only)

Small but very popular restaurant with a lived-in feel and seating
for just twenty guests. The set menu offers three choices per course
and is supplemented by blackboard specials; cooking is Finnish and
follows the seasons.

LYON ⫶○

FRENCH • BISTRO

Mannerheimintie 56 ⊠ 00260 **PLAN: A1**
TEL. 010 3281560 – **www**.ravintolalyon.fi
Closed July, Easter, Christmas, midsummer, Sunday and Monday
Menu 58€ – Carte 61/73€ (dinner only)

Well-established restaurant with a traditional bistro feel; set across
from the Opera House. Wide-ranging menus offer seasonal French
dishes crafted from Finnish ingredients. These are accompanied by
a small French wine selection.

MURU ⅟○

MODERN CUISINE • NEIGHBOURHOOD •
TRENDY   ⅟ 🍴 🎴 |A/C| ⇥

Fredrikinkatu 41 ✉ 00120 PLAN: B2
Ⓜ Kamppi
TEL. 0300 472335 (booking essential) – www.murudining.fi
Closed Christmas, New Year, Easter, 1 May, midsummer, Sunday,
Monday and bank holidays
Menu 52€ – Carte 46/52€ (dinner only)

Three passionate young owners and a charming, chatty team
have created a vibrant, welcoming spot. It's cosy and rustic with a
contemporary edge, and displays quirky wine-themed lighting and
a bar made from old wine boxes. Cooking is refined yet gutsy; there
are two sittings for dinner and booking is a must.

NOKKA ⅟○

MODERN CUISINE • ELEGANT   ⅟⅟ 🍴 |A/C| ⇥ ⬭

Kanavaranta 7F ✉ 00160 PLAN: D2
TEL. 09 61285600 – www.ravintolanokka.fi
Closed Christmas-New Year, Easter, midsummer,
6 December and Sunday
Menu 50€ (weekday lunch)/66€ – Carte 48/78€

Converted harbourside warehouse with a nautical feel – look out for
the huge anchor and propeller. There's a cookery school, a wine cellar
and a smart glass-walled kitchen. Modern Finnish cooking relies on
small farm producers.

PASSIO ⅈⅉ○

MODERN CUISINE • FRIENDLY • NEIGHBOURHOOD ✗ AC

Kalevankatu 13 ✉ 00100 PLAN: B2
Ⓜ Kamppi
TEL. 020 7352040 (booking advisable) – **www**.passiodining.fi
Closed Christmas and midsummer
Menu 29/50€ (dinner only) (surprise menu only)

With its exposed ducts, dimly lit lamps and leather-topped tables,
Passio has a faux industrial look. 3 or 5 course 'Surprise' menus
feature regional ingredients. It's run by a local brewer, so be sure to
try the artisan beers.

PASTIS ⅈⅉ○

CLASSIC FRENCH • BISTRO • NEIGHBOURHOOD ✗ AC ⅋

Pieni Roobertinkatu 2 ✉ 00130 PLAN: C2
TEL. 0300 472336 (booking essential) – **www**.pastis.fi
Closed Easter, Christmas and Sunday
Menu 30/50€ – Carte 43/56€

The clue is in the name: they serve classic French dishes, alongside
several different brands of pastis. It's a popular place, so there's
always a lively atmosphere. Come for Saturday brunch or have a
private meal in Petit Pastis.

RAGU ⑪○

MODERN CUISINE • DESIGN • CHIC   XX ⅙ AC ⇔

Ludviginkatu 3-5 ✉ 00130 **PLAN: C2**
Ⓜ Rautatientori
TEL. 09 596659 (booking advisable) – **www**.ragu.fi
Closed July, Easter, midsummer, Christmas and Sunday
Menu 45€ – Carte 49/56€ (dinner only)

Finland's famed seasonal ingredients are used in unfussy Italian recipes and the welcoming service and lively atmosphere also have something of an Italian feel. Choose the weekly 'House' menu to sample the latest produce to arrive.

REGINA ⑪○

MODERN CUISINE • INTIMATE • NEIGHBOURHOOD   X AC

Neitsytpolku 10 ✉ 00140 **PLAN: C3**
TEL. 010 5014696 – **www**.restaurantregina.fi
Closed Sunday-Tuesday
Carte 44/64€ (dinner only)

This small, cosy bistro sits in a residential area and has a friendly, bustling feel. Unfussy international dishes change every two weeks and showcase produce from all over Europe. The wine list is thoughtfully compiled.

SALUTORGET ⭐️🍴

INTERNATIONAL • BRASSERIE • ELEGANT   ✕✕ ♿ AC ⟊

Pohjoisesplanadi 15 ✉ 00170 PLAN: C2
Ⓜ Kaisaniemi
TEL. 09 61285950 – **www**.salutorget.fi
Closed Easter, Christmas, midsummer and bank holidays
Menu 39€ (weekday lunch)/49€ – Carte 39/56€

An old bank, located on the esplanade; now an elegant restaurant
with impressive columns and attractive stained glass. The classic,
brasserie-style menu has global influences. Have afternoon tea in
the plush cocktail bar.

SAVOY 🍴

MODERN CUISINE • ELEGANT   ✕✕✕ 🍸 ⟋ ♿ 🏠 AC ⟊ ⬭

Eteläesplanadi 14 (8th floor) ✉ 00130 PLAN: C2
Ⓜ Kaisaniemi
TEL. 09 61285330 – **www**.royalravintolat.com/savoy
Closed Easter, Christmas, Saturday lunch and Sunday
Menu 68€ (lunch) – Carte 83/97€

The city's most famous restaurant opened in 1937 and offers
impressive views from its 8th floor setting. Choose from updated
versions of old favourites or a seasonal 4 course menu of refined,
attractively presented modern dishes.

SPIS ⫩◍

MODERN CUISINE • NEIGHBOURHOOD • BISTRO   ✗ ⇔

Kasarmikatu 26 ✉ 00130 **PLAN: C2**
TEL. 045 3051211 (booking essential) – **www**.spis.fi
Closed Sunday, Monday and bank holidays
Menu 50/77€ (dinner only) (tasting menu only)

Intimate restaurant seating just 18; the décor is 'faux derelict', with
exposed brick and plaster walls. Creative, flavoursome cooking
features Nordic flavours in attractive, imaginative combinations. Most
dishes are vegetable-based.

TOCA ⫩◍

MODERN CUISINE • TRENDY   ✗ ⇔

Unioninkatu 18 ✉ 00130 **PLAN: C2**
TEL. 044 2379922 (booking essential) – **www**.toca.fi
Closed July, 22 December-8 January, Sunday and Monday
Menu 65€ (dinner only and lunch Tuesday-Thursday-set menu only
at dinner)

Modest little bistro with an unfinished look. At lunch they serve just
two dishes – aimed at local workers – while dinner offers a 3 or 5
set course menu. Cooking is an original mix of Italian simplicity and
Finnish modernity.

YUME ⭐

ASIAN · DESIGN · FASHIONABLE

Kämp Hotel · Kluuvikatu 2 ✉ 00100 PLAN: C2
Ⓜ Kaisaniemi
TEL. 09 57611718 – **www**.hotelkamp.fi
Closed Christmas, Easter, Sunday and Monday
Menu 54/62€ – Carte 47/62€ (dinner only)

Sit on the large heated terrace or head for the comfy modern dining
room, which is divided up by ornate wooden frames. Alongside Asian-
inspired dishes with a Californian twist, you'll find a selection of sushi,
sashimi and nigiri.

KÄMP

GRAND LUXURY · CLASSIC

Pohjoisesplanadi 29 ✉ 00100 PLAN: C2
Ⓜ Kaisaniemi
TEL. 09 576111 – **www**.hotelkamp.fi
179 rm ☕ – 🛏 340/670€ 🛏🛏 370/970€ – 8 suites
YUME – See restaurant listing

The grand façade, columned interior and impressive staircase point
back to this luxurious hotel's 19C roots and the classically furnished
bedrooms follow suit; the superb spa, meanwhile, adds a modern
touch. The chic bar offers an excellent selection of champagne and
cocktails, while for dining, there's Asian-inspired 'Yume' or a bustling
brasserie with a global menu.

CROWNE PLAZA HELSINKI

BUSINESS • CHAIN • CONTEMPORARY

Mannerheimintie 50 ✉ 00260 **PLAN: A1**
TEL. 09 25210000 – **www**.crowneplaza-helsinki.fi
349 rm ☲ – ♦ 145/492€ ♦♦ 145/492€ – 4 suites

Spacious hotel specialising in conferences. Comfy, up-to-date bedrooms have good facilities and city or lake views; the higher the floor, the better the grade. Pay a visit to the huge basement fitness club and spa, then make for the warm, welcoming restaurant which serves Mediterranean cuisine.

HILTON HELSINKI STRAND

BUSINESS • LUXURY • CLASSIC

John Stenbergin Ranta 4 ✉ 00530 **PLAN: C1**
Ⓜ Hakaniemi
TEL. 09 39351 – **www**.hilton.com
190 rm – ♦ 129/360€ ♦♦ 165/395€, ☲ 22€ – 7 suites

This spacious waterfront hotel has a classical 1980s design, an impressive atrium and an 8th floor fitness and relaxation centre; take in the view from the gym or pool. Smartly kept bedrooms boast marble bathrooms – ask for a room overlooking the water. The restaurant offers global classics and local specialities.

CENTRE

GLO HOTEL KLUUVI

LUXURY • MODERN • DESIGN

Kluuvikatu 4 ⊠ 00100 PLAN: C2
Ⓜ Kaisaniemi
TEL. 010 3444400 – **www**.glohotels.fi
184 rm ⌖ – 👤 125/370€ 👥 135/380€ – 6 suites

Stylish hotel on a fashionable shopping street; a boutique sister to
next door Kämp, whose spa it shares. Spacious bedrooms have a
contemporary look and come with smart glass shower rooms. There's
also a lively bar-lounge and a fashionable restaurant serving cuisine
from around the globe.

HAVEN

BUSINESS • LUXURY • MODERN

Unioninkatu 17 ⊠ 00130 PLAN: C2
TEL. 09 681930 – **www**.hotelhaven.fi
77 rm ⌖ – 👤 199/270€ 👥 219/290€

Centrally located office block conversion with an elegant townhouse-
style interior and clubby bar offering a great rum selection. Chic
bedrooms have top quality furnishings and marble bathrooms with
TVs. Have breakfast overlooking the harbour, then at night dine on
Russian cuisine in Bystro or in the Nordic fine dining restaurant.

HOLIDAY INN HELSINKI WEST RUOHOLAHTI

BUSINESS • FUNCTIONAL

🏃 🐎 🕌 💆 AC 💇 🏊

Sulhasenkuja 3 ✉ 00180 PLAN: A3
Ⓜ Ruoholahti
TEL. 09 41521000 – www.holidayinn.com
Closed Saturday, Sunday and lunch bank holidays
256 rm ☷ – 🛉 65/220€ 🛉🛉 80/235€

Set outside the city on a business park but close to a metro station.
Modern bedrooms display touches of colour and come with compact
shower rooms and excellent soundproofing; the higher, west-facing
rooms have pleasant water and city views. The light, bright restaurant
serves international cuisine.

KLAUS K

LUXURY • DESIGN

🏃 🕌 💆 AC 💇 🏊

Bulevardi 2/4 ✉ 00120 PLAN: C2
Ⓜ Rautatientori
TEL. 020 7704703 – www.klauskhotel.com
171 rm ☷ – 🛉 120/320€ 🛉🛉 140/640€

A landmark building with a funky, laid-back vibe and a striking interior
designed to reflect the themes of The Kalevala. Bedroom styles
include 'Passion', 'Mystical', 'Desire' and 'Envy'; the top floor 'Sky
Lofts' are particularly sumptuous. Modern Tuscan cuisine is served
under an embossed metal ceiling.

LILLA ROBERTS

BUSINESS • DESIGN • PERSONALISED

⛲ ♿ ♨ 🅰️Ⓒ

Pieni Roobertinkatu 1-3 ✉ 00130 PLAN: C2
TEL. 09 6899880 – www.lillaroberts.fi
130 rm 🛏 – 🧍150/330€ 🧍‍🧍180/360€ – 1 suite

The building was designed in 1908 by one of Finland's top architects
and was originally head office for the city's energy works. The smart,
designer interior uses dark colours and is centred around the concept
of 'hygge' (enjoying the simple things in life). The elegant restaurant
serves an appealing menu.

RADISSON BLU PLAZA

BUSINESS • CHAIN • CONTEMPORARY

⛲ ♿ 🏊 ♨ 🅰️Ⓒ 🍽 🛗

Mikonkatu 23 ✉ 00100 PLAN: C2
Ⓜ Kaisaniemi
TEL. 020 1234703 – www.radissonblu.com/plazahotel-helsinki
302 rm 🛏 – 🧍139/389€ 🧍‍🧍149/399€ – 1 suite

Elegant 20C building set close to the station and completed by a more
modern wing. Well-equipped bedrooms come in a choice of modern
or classic styles and many have 3D TVs. The bar is a fashionable spot
and the large restaurant – unusually set over several rooms – offers
five different types of cuisine.

TORNI

BUSINESS · ART DÉCO · ELEGANT

Yrjönkatu 26 ⊠ 00100 PLAN: B2
Ⓜ Rautatientori
TEL. 020 1234604 – **www**.sokoshoteltorni.fi
152 rm ⌷ – **♦** 179/269€ **♦♦** 179/269€ – 6 suites

Charming early 20C hotel with a palpable sense of history. Bedrooms come in 'Art Deco', 'Art Nouveau' and 'Functionalist' styles – the latter, in the 11 storey tower, have glass-walled bathrooms. The top floor bar has a terrace and superb city views; the restaurant offers traditional Finnish cuisine.

FABIAN

TOWNHOUSE · CONTEMPORARY · MODERN

Fabiankatu 7 ⊠ 00130 PLAN: C2
TEL. 09 61282000 – **www**.hotelfabian.fi
58 rm ⌷ – **♦** 139/250€ **♦♦** 169/350€

Charming boutique hotel close to the harbour. Bedrooms have stylish black & white themes and smart bathrooms with heated floors. Have breakfast in the central courtyard in summer – ingredients are organic or from small producers.

GLO HOTEL ART

TOWNHOUSE • BUSINESS • MODERN

Lönnrotinkatu 29 ⊠ 00180 PLAN: B3
Ⓜ Kamppi
TEL. 010 3444100 – www.glohotels.fi
171 rm ☕ – ♦ 150/300€ ♦♦ 165/365€

Sited in the heart of the lively Design District, a 1903 art nouveau castle with modern extensions and its own art collection. Chic bedrooms were styled by Finnish designers and come in three sizes. You can borrow everything from bicycles to paints and brushes. A Nordic grill menu is served in the old cellars.

KATAJANOKKA

HISTORIC • GRAND LUXURY

Merikasarminkatu 1 ⊠ 00160 PLAN: D2
TEL. 09 686450 – www.hotelkatajanokka.fi
106 rm ☕ – ♦ 99/219€ ♦♦ 109/229€

A pleasantly restored, late 19C prison with its original staircases and high ceilinged corridors still on display. The old cells are now comfortable, well-equipped bedrooms with modern bathrooms. The traditional cellar restaurant features a preserved prison cell and serves traditional Finnish cuisine.

ALBERT

BUSINESS • CONTEMPORARY

👤 ♿ ♨ AC ⊬

Albertinkatu 30 ✉ 00180 **PLAN: B3**
TEL. 020 1234638 – **www**.sokoshotels.fi
Closed Christmas
95 rm ☒ – 🧍 129/185€ 🧍🧍 144/195€

An unassuming 19C building with a contrastingly cosy interior.
Good-sized contemporary bedrooms are well-equipped and come
with Nordic furniture and up-to-date bathrooms. Have drinks in the
welcoming open-plan lounge-bar, then head to the trattoria-style
restaurant for a selection of Italian classics.

RIVOLI JARDIN

TOWNHOUSE • COSY • PERSONALISED

♿ ♨ ⊬

Kasarmikatu 40 ✉ 00130 **PLAN: C2**
TEL. 09 681500 – **www**.rivoli.fi
Closed Christmas
55 rm ☒ – 🧍 100/240€ 🧍🧍 120/260€

A small, city centre oasis hidden away off a courtyard, with an intimate
conservatory lounge, and a sauna and meeting room tucked away in
the cellar. Bedrooms are cosy and individually decorated; those on
the top floor have terraces.

HILTON HELSINKI AIRPORT

BUSINESS • MODERN

👨‍🍳 ♿ 🏊 🛁 AC ⇆ 🧖 **P**

Lentàjànkuja 1 (North: 19 km by A 137) ✉ 01530
TEL. 09 73220 – **www**.hilton.com
330 rm – 🛉 99/370€ 🛉🛉 109/400€, ⛁ 27€ – 5 suites

3mins from the international terminal (T2); a spacious glass hotel
with a relaxed ambience and a large conference capacity. Well-
soundproofed bedrooms boast locally designed furniture, good
facilities and large bathrooms – some have saunas. The stylish
restaurant serves Finnish and international cuisine.

KASKIS 🍴○

MODERN CUISINE • FRIENDLY • NEIGHBOURHOOD   ✗ AC

Kaskenkatu 6a ✉ 20700
TEL. 045 6723197 (booking essential) – **www**.kaskis.fi
Closed Christmas, midsummer, Sunday and Monday
Menu 45/59€ (dinner only)

 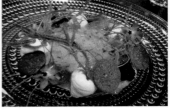

This bright glass-fronted restaurant has a lively, fun atmosphere. The
concise à la carte offers traditional Finnish recipes prepared in a
modern manner and the 6 course Surprise menu is a great way to
sample a range of dishes.

katiisoup/iStock

ICELAND

AWARDS

REYKJAVIK
ICELAND

marchello74/iStock

Europe's youngest landmass is a country of extremes; a dramatic wilderness where volcanic springs sit beside vast glaciers and long summer days are offset by dark winters. Its largest city, Reykjavik, lays claim to being the world's most northern capital and its settlement by a Norseman over 1100 years ago is recounted in the Icelandic Sagas.

Two thirds of Icelanders live in Reykjavik, in low, colourful buildings designed to fend off the North Atlantic winds and brighten spirits through the long, dark nights. Other buildings

echo nature itself: the geometric shapes of the Hallgrímskirkja Church – whose soaring tower keeps watch over the city – mirror the lava flows, while the Harpa Concert Hall is cleverly designed to reflect both the city and nature – its cascading LEDs alluding to the incredible spectacle of the Aurora Borealis.

The historic city centre, known as 101, lies between the harbour and an inland lake, and is a bustling, bohemian place filled with independent boutiques and fashionable bars. Head out further east and you can discover the secrets of the Blue Lagoon's healing thermal waters and the Golden Circle, which comprises three of Iceland's greatest natural wonders: the Þingvellir National Park (where you can walk between two tectonic plates); the Haukadalur Geothermal Field with its geysers and mud pools; and the spectacular Gullfoss Waterfall – the largest in Europe.

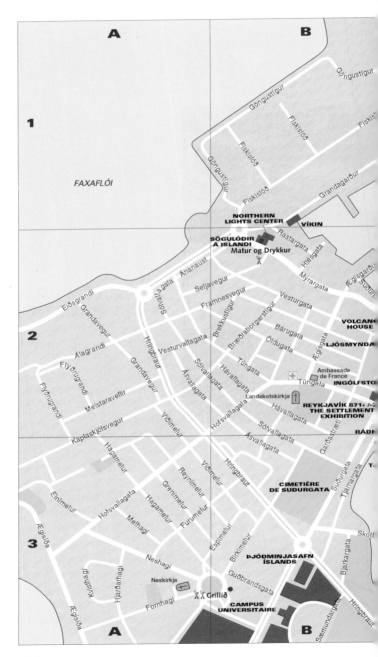

A B

1

FAXAFLÓI

NORTHERN LIGHTS CENTER VÍKIN
SÖGULÓDIR Á ÍSLANDI
Matur og Drykkur
Rastargata
Hlésgata
Myrargata
Ægisgarður
Suðurt...

2

Eiðsgrandi
Grandavegur
Ananaust
Seljavegur
Framnesvegur
Vesturgata
VOLCANO HOUSE
Álagrandi
Hringbraut
Vesturvallagata
Brekkustígur
Bræðraborgarstígur
Bárugata
Öldugata
Ægisgata
LJÓSMYNDA
Flyðrugrandi
Grandavegur
Ásvallagata
Sólvallagata
Túngata
Hávallagata
Túngata
Ambassade de France
INGÓLFSTO...
Meistaravellir
Flyðrugrandi
Viðimelur
Hofsvallagata
Landakotskirkja
Hávallagata
REYKJAVÍK 871+ /-2
THE SETTLEMENT EXHIBITION
Kaplaskjólsvegur
Sólvallagata
Ásvallagata
Garðastræti
RÁÐ...

Hagamelur
Reynimelur
Viðimelur
Hringbraut
Suðurgata
Tjarnargata
T...
Einimelur
Grenimelur
Hagamelur
Furumelur
CIMETIÈRE DE SUÐURGATA
Melhagi
Bjarkargata
Skot...

3
Ægisíða
Espimelur
Birkimelur
ÞJÓÐMINJASAFN ÍSLANDS
Neshagi
Guðbrandsgata
Hjarðarhagi
Kvisthagi
Neskirkja
Fornhagi
Grillið
CAMPUS UNIVERSITAIRE
Samundargata
Hringbrau...

A B

122

Reykjavik Centre

C

D

0 — 200 m

1

FAXAFLÓI

2

Eyjarslóð

PORT

HARPA

ISTASAFN
YKJAVÍKUR

KOLAPORTID

ryggvagata

afnarstræti

ISTASAFN

STJÓRNARRÁDID

ARNARHÓLL

URVÖLLUR

101

Borg

DÓMKIRKJAN

MENNTASKÓLINN

Canopy
by Hilton

ATRE
NÓ

FRÍKIRKJAN

LISTASAFN
ÍSLANDS

Gallery

Hellusund

Holt

Fjólugata

Sóleyjargata

Njardargata

Bergstadastræti

LISTASAFN
EINARS JÓNSSONAR

LISTASAFN ASÍ

Mímisvegur

Geirsgata

Faxagata

Ingólfsstræti

Skúlagata

Sölvhólsgata

Sæbraut

PJÓDMENNINGARHÚSID

PJÓDLEIKHÚSID

Laugavegur

A-HÚS

Dill

Hverfisgata

Lindargata

Skúlagata

Sæbraut

SUN-CRAFT

Vatnsstígur

NÝLISTASAFNID

Sæbraut

Skúlagata

Hverfisgata

SÆBRAUT

Snorrabraut

Laugavegur

Klapparstígur

Grettisgata

Frakkastígur

Óðinsgata

Týsgata

Njálsgata

Skólavörðustígur

Lokastígur

Pórsgata

Freyjugata

Baldursgata

Bragagata

Vitastígur

Alda

Grettisgata

Barónsstígur

Njálsgata

REDASAFN

Laugavegur

Grettisgata

Njálsgata

Bergpórugata

HALLGRÍMSKIRKJA

Barónsstígur

Egilsgata

Leifsgata

Laufásvegur

Miðstræti

Pingholtsstræti

Bergstaðastræti

Laufásvegur

● Hotel
● Restaurant

3

123

REYKJAVÍK

DILL 🌸

CREATIVE • RUSTIC • INTIMATE   XX ✔ 🏠

Hverfisgötu 12 ✉ 101 PLAN: C2
TEL. 552 1522 (booking essential) – **www**.dillrestaurant.is
Closed Sunday-Tuesday
Menu 11900/13900 ISK (dinner only) (tasting menu only)

Chef:
Ragnar Eiriksson
Specialities:
Arctic char, celery and watercress.
Wild goose, salsify and berries.
Broken blueberry pie.

This small, dimly-lit restaurant has become a favourite destination for New Nordic cooking. It resembles an old barn, and the best of the island's ingredients are skilfully prepared at the central counter. Each dish uses just a handful of ingredients but demonstrates complexity in its textures and flavours.

MATUR OG DRYKKUR 😊

TRADITIONAL CUISINE • SIMPLE • TRENDY   X ♿ ✔ **P**

Grandagarður 2 ✉ 101 PLAN: B2
TEL. 571 8877 – **www**.maturogdrykkur.is
Closed Monday dinner and Sunday
Menu 3490/5990 ISK – Carte 5300/7800 ISK

This simple little eatery is named after a famous Icelandic cookbook and shares its premises with the Saga Museum. Old recipes are given subtle modern twists, with delicious dishes displaying touches of creativity. Alongside the à la carte are some great value set menus; be sure to order some 'snacks' too.

GALLERY ⭑⭐

MODERN CUISINE • CLASSIC DÉCOR •
INTIMATE

Holt Hotel, Bergstadastraeti 37 ⊠ 101 PLAN: C3
TEL. 552 5700 (booking essential) – **www**.holt.is
Closed Sunday and Monday
Menu 3900/14900 ISK – Carte 7650/13500 ISK

The island's oldest and most highly regarded restaurant sits within
the Holt hotel, and comes with red furniture and a huge art collection.
Classic French cooking uses top island produce; the cured salmon
recipe dates back to 1966!

GRILLIÐ ⭑⭐

MODERN CUISINE • CLASSIC DÉCOR •
ELEGANT

Radisson Blue Saga Hotel, Hagatorg ⊠ 107 PLAN: B3
TEL. 525 9900 (booking essential) – **www**.radissonblu.com
Closed Sunday-Monday
Menu 10500/12500 ISK (dinner only) (tasting menu only)

Located at the top of a hotel; the unusual ceiling depicts the zodiac
signs but it's the 360° views that will steal your attention, especially
at sunset. The young team deliver an array of ambitious Nordic dishes
with clear flavours.

VOX

MODERN CUISINE • CONTEMPORARY DÉCOR • ELEGANT

Hilton Reykjavik Nordica Hotel, Suðurlandsbraut 2
(East: 2.75 km by 41) ✉ 108
TEL. 444 5050 - **www**.vox.is
Menu 8900 ISK - Carte 9800/13200 ISK

A stylish restaurant and bar set off the lobby of the Hilton hotel. At lunch there's a popular hot and cold buffet; at dinner, choices include an à la carte and 'Season' and 'Seafood' tasting menus. Cooking is modern and creative.

101

LUXURY • DESIGN • TRENDY

Hverfisgata 10 ✉ 101 **PLAN: C2**
TEL. 580 0101 - **www**.101hotel.is
38 rm - † 41300/106000 ISK †† 41300/106000 ISK

Behind the unassuming façade of the former Social Democratic Party offices, you'll find this sleek design hotel filled with interesting Icelandic art. Stylish monochrome bedrooms have stunning glass bathrooms; choose one with a balcony or a harbour view. The stylish restaurant with its long bar and glass ceiling is the perfect spot to try modern Icelandic cooking.

BORG

LUXURY • ART DÉCO • ELEGANT

Pósthússtræti 11 ⊠ 101 **PLAN: C2**
TEL. 5511440 – **www**.keahotels.is
99 rm ⌥ – **♦** 28000/65000 ISK **♦♦** 35000/67500 ISK – 2 suites

Overlooking Austurvöllur Square is this carefully restored 1930s hotel which combines traditional elegance with modern comforts. Bedrooms encapsulate the art deco era with bespoke furnishings, wooden floors and elegant lines. The bar has a charming square counter and doubles as a restaurant.

CANOPY BY HILTON

BOUTIQUE HOTEL • CONTEMPORARY • TRENDY

Smidjustigur 4 ⊠ 101 **PLAN: C2/3**
TEL. 528 7000 – **www**.canopybyhilton.com
112 rm ⌥ – **♦** 29000/69000 ISK **♦♦** 29000/69000 ISK – 8 suites

The first ever 'Canopy' sits just off the main street. It's a relaxed and stylish home-from-home; grab breakfast in the deli, borrow a bike or take in city views from the top floor terrace. Understated bedrooms feature natural materials, bespoke furniture and quirky artwork. Menus offer creative small plates.

HOLT

FAMILY • CLASSIC • COSY

Bergstadastraeti 37 ✉ 101 **PLAN: C3**
TEL. 552 5700 - **www**.holt.is
42 rm ☕ - 🚹 38000/48000 ISK 👥 38000/48000 ISK - 4 suites
GALLERY - See restaurant listing

The draws of this family-run hotel are its old world charm and quiet suburban location. The 4th floor bedrooms look out over the city, while the cosy lounge and cocktail bar are great places to appreciate their vast art collection.

ALDA

BOUTIQUE HOTEL • CONTEMPORARY • TRENDY

Laugavegi 66-68 ✉ 101 **PLAN: D3**
TEL. 553 9366 - **www**.aldahotel.is
88 rm ☕ - 🚹 21200/47000 ISK 👥 21200/47000 ISK - 2 suites

At the quieter eastern end of the main shopping street you'll find this fashionable hotel complete with its own barber's shop and trendy bar offering simple meals. Bedrooms are simply but stylishly furnished with natural materials like Icelandic wool; the 4th floor rooms have balconies with sea views.

J. Arnold Images/hemis.fr

NORWAY

AWARDS

OSLO

Norway

J. Frumm/hemis.fr

Oslo has a lot going for it – and one slight downside: it's one of the world's most expensive cities. It also ranks high when it comes to its standard of living, however, and its position at the head of Oslofjord, surrounded by steep forested hills, is hard to match for drama and beauty. It's a charmingly compact place to stroll round, particularly in the summer, when the daylight hours practically abolish the night and, although it may lack the urban cool of some other Scandinavian cities, it boasts its fair share of trendy clubs and a raft of Michelin Stars. There's a real raft,

too: Thor Hyerdahl's famous Kon-Tiki – one of the star turns in a city that loves its museums. Oslo's uncluttered feel is enhanced by parks and wide streets and, in the winter, there are times when you feel you have the whole place to yourself. Drift into the city by boat and land at the smart harbour of Aker Brygge; to the west lies the charming Bygdøy peninsula, home to museums permeated with the smell of the sea. Northwest is Frogner, with its famous sculpture park, the place where locals hang out on long summer days. The centre of town, the commercial hub, is Karl Johans Gate, bounded at one end by the Royal Palace and at the other by the Cathedral, while further east lie two trendy multicultural areas, Grunerlokka and Grønland, the former also home to the Edvard Munch Museum.

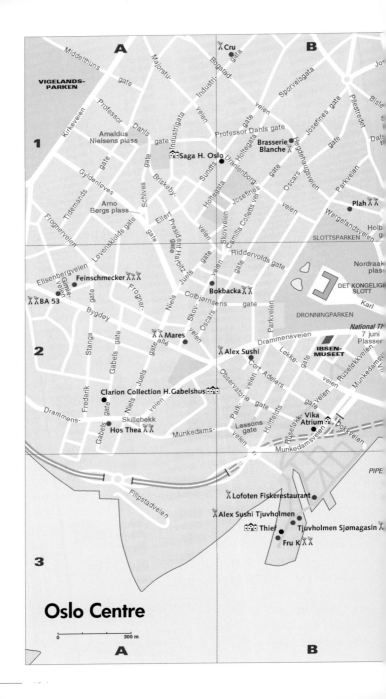

Oslo Centre

0 _____ 300 m

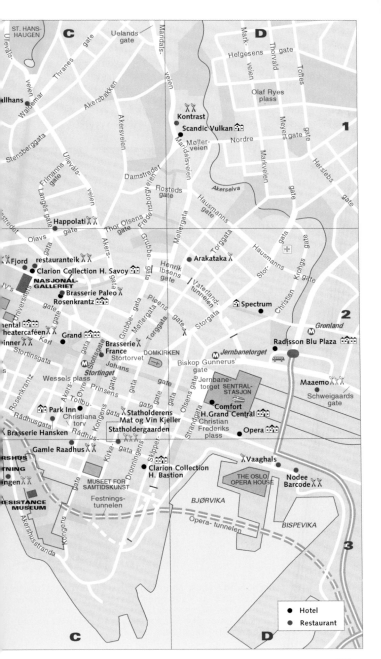

ST. HANS-
HAUGEN
C
Uelands gate

D

Mark-
veien

Helgesens gate

Thorvald gate

Toftes gate

Waldemar
Thranes gate

Olaf Ryes
plass

1

Ullevals-
veien

Akersbakken

Meyers gate

Nordre

Markveien

Herslebs gate

Stensberggata

Frimanns gate

Akersveien

Maridalsveien

Kontrast

Scandic Vulkan 🏨

Møller-
veien

Ullevals-
veien

Damstredet

Rosteds gate

Akerselva

Hausmanns gate

Langes gate

Fredensborgveien

Happolati ✂✂

Olavs gata

Thor Olsens gate

Akers-
gata

Mølleralata

Torggata

Stor-

Hausmanns gate

Christian Krohgs gate

✂ Fjord   restauranteik ✂✂

Clarion Collection H. Savoy 🏨

Henrik
Ibsens
gate

Arakataka ✂

NASJONAL-
GALLERIET

Brasserie Paleo ✂

Vaterland-
tunnelen

🏨 Spectrum

2

Rosenkrantz 🏨

Pløens gate

Grubbe- gata

nental 🏨
theatercaféen ✂✂
inner ✂✂ Karl

Grand 🏨

Møllergata

Torggata

Storgata

Grønland Ⓜ

Radisson Blu Plaza 🏨

Stortingsgata

Johans gata

Brasserie ✂
France

Stortorvet

DOMKIRKEN

Biskop Gunnerus'
gate

Maaemo ✂✂✂

Rosenkrantz

Akers- gata

Stortings Ⓜ
Stortinget

Johans

gate

Jernbanetorget Ⓜ

Jernbane-
torget SENTRAL-
STASJON

Schweigaards
gate

Wessels plass

Prinsens gate

Olsens gate

Park Inn 🏨

Tollbu- gata

Christiania
torv

Kongens gata ✂ Statholderens
Mat og Vin Kjeller

Comfort
H.Grand Central 🏨

Strandata

Rådhusgata

Rådhus-
gata

Statholdergaarden
✂✂✂

Christian
Frederiks
plass

Opera 🏨

Brasserie Hansken ✂

Gamle Raadhus ✂✂

Kirke- gata

Dronningens gate

Skipper- gata

ARHUS
TNING
ingen ✂✂

✂Vaaghals

Clarion Collection
H. Bastion 🏨

THE OSLO
OPERA HOUSE

Nodee
Barcode ✂✂

RESISTANCE
MUSEUM

MUSEET FOR
SAMTIDSKUNST

Festnings-
tunnelen

BJØRVIKA

Akershusstranda

Kongens gate

BISPEVIKA

Opera- tunnelen

3

● Hotel
● Restaurant

C

D

MAAEMO ✿✿✿

MODERN CUISINE • DESIGN • FASHIONABLE   XxX AC

Schweigaardsgate 15b (entrance via staircase) ✉ 0191 PLAN: D2
Ⓜ Grønland
TEL. 22 17 99 69 (booking essential) – www.maaemo.no
Closed Easter, 16-18 May, mid December to mid January and
Sunday-Tuesday

Menu 2600 NOK (dinner only and lunch Friday-Saturday)
(tasting menu only)

Chef:
Esben Holmboe Bang
Specialities:
Oyster emulsion with mussels and
dill. Reindeer with preserved plum
sauce and artichokes. Brown butter
ice cream, molasses and roasted
hazelnuts.

A striking, modern restaurant with an intimate, brightly lit interior and
an unusual mezzanine-level kitchen; dishes are finished at the table,
with some are presented by the chefs themselves. Maaemo means
'Mother Earth' and top quality Norwegian produce guides the 20+
course menu; cooking is intricate, original and visually stimulating
with some sublime flavour combinations.

KONTRAST ✿

SCANDINAVIAN • DESIGN • FASHIONABLE   XX & AC ✦

Maridalsveien 15 ✉ 0178 PLAN: D1
TEL. 21 60 01 01 – www.restaurant-kontrast.no
Closed Christmas, New Year, Easter, last week July- first week
August, Sunday and Monday

Menu 795/1450 NOK – Carte 460/630 NOK (dinner only)

Chef:
Mikael Svenssen
Specialities:
Scallops with roe emulsion and
nasturtium. Salt-baked chicken with
meadowsweet gel. Strawberries
with rosehip cream and whipped
duck eggs.

A modern restaurant with a stark, semi-industrial feel created by the
concrete floor, exposed pipework and open kitchen. Seasonal, organic
Norwegian produce is used to create refined, original, full-flavoured
dishes whose apparent simplicity often masks their complex nature.
Service is well-paced and professional.

STATHOLDERGAARDEN ✿

CLASSIC CUISINE • CHIC • ELEGANT   XxX 🍴 🖧

Rådhusgata 11 (entrance on Kirkegata) ✉ 0151 PLAN: C3
Ⓜ Stortinget
TEL. 22 41 88 00 (booking essential) – **www**.statholdergaarden.no
Closed 17 July-8 August, Christmas, Easter, Sunday and bank
holidays
Menu 1095 NOK – Carte 925/1080 NOK (dinner only)

Chef:
Bent Stiansen
Specialities:
Scallop and salmon with spring
cabbage and ceps. Rib-eye of
veal with Jerusalem artichoke and
tarragon sauce. Raspberry and
chocolate.

A charming 17C house in the city's heart. Three elegant rooms feature
an array of antiques and curios, and have wonderfully ornate stucco
ceilings hung with chandeliers. Expertly rendered classical cooking
uses seasonal Norwegian ingredients in familiar combinations.
Service is well-versed and willing.

RESTAURANTEIK 👀

MODERN CUISINE • FASHIONABLE •
BRASSERIE   XX A/C 🖧

Clarion Collection H. Savoy • Universitetsgata 11 ✉ 0164 PLAN: C2
Ⓜ National Theatret
TEL. 22 36 07 10 – **www**.restauranteik.no
Closed July, Easter, Christmas, Sunday and Monday
Menu 395 NOK (dinner only) (tasting menu only)

A contemporary L-shaped dining room in a hotel close to the National
Gallery. It's minimalist in style, with colourful artwork, an open
kitchen and a glass-walled wine cellar. The weekly 3-5 course set
menu comprises inventive international cuisine. Service is efficient
and the atmosphere is friendly.

SMALHANS

TRADITIONAL • NEIGHBOURHOOD • SIMPLE

Waldemar Thranes gate 10A ✉ 0171 **PLAN: C1**
TEL. 22 69 60 00 – **www**.smalhans.no
Closed 3 weeks July, Easter, Christmas and Monday
Menu 425/615 NOK – Carte lunch 315/420 NOK

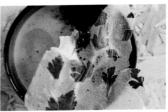

A sweet neighbourhood café with friendly staff and an urban feel. Coffee and homemade cakes are served in the morning, with a short selection of dishes including soup and a burger on offer between 12pm and 4pm. A daily hot dish is available from 4-6pm, while set menus and sharing plates are served at dinner.

ALEX SUSHI

JAPANESE • DESIGN • MINIMALIST

Cort Adelers Gate 2 ✉ 0254 **PLAN: B2**
Ⓜ National Theatret
TEL. 22 43 99 99 – **www**.alexsushi.no
Closed July, Easter and Christmas
Menu 485 NOK – Carte 195/860 NOK (dinner only)

A glass-fronted Japanese restaurant and takeaway, with a bright interior made of wood, steel and glass. Sit at the boat-shaped sushi bar to try top quality local sashimi. Half of customers choose the set menus, which offer the best value.

ALEX SUSHI TJUVHOLMEN ⅃○

SUSHI • SIMPLE • NEIGHBOURHOOD

Strandpromenaden 11 ⊠ 0252 **PLAN: B3**
TEL. 22 43 99 99 – **www**.alexsushi.no
Closed Easter, Christmas and Sunday
Menu 495/995 NOK – Carte lunch 320/425 NOK

Set in a fantastic harbourside spot, with a great terrace. The skilful, knowledgeable chefs are surrounded by large scuba diver models. Sushi, sashimi and nigiri feature at lunch, followed by 3 set menus at dinner. The tuna is superb.

ARAKATAKA ⅃○

NORWEGIAN • FASHIONABLE • FRIENDLY

Mariboes gate 7 ⊠ 0183 **PLAN: D2**
Ⓜ Stortinget
TEL. 23 32 83 00 (booking advisable) – **www**.arakataka.no
Closed July, Christmas and Easter
Menu 495/565 NOK – Carte 410/510 NOK (dinner only)

A smart glass-fronted restaurant with a central food bar, an open kitchen and a buzzy atmosphere. Choose from a concise menu of seasonal Norwegian small plates – they recommend 3 savoury dishes plus a dessert per person.

BA 53 🍴

MODERN CUISINE • FASHIONABLE •
NEIGHBOURHOOD

XX 🏠 AC ⇔

Bygdoy Allé 53 ✉ 0265 PLAN: A2
TEL. 21 42 05 90 – **www**.ba53.no
Closed Christmas, July and Sunday
Menu 535/875 NOK – Carte 530/730 NOK
(Monday to Friday dinner only)

A daytime coffee shop combines with a moody cocktail bar and
a relaxed, softly lit brasserie to create this stylish neighbourhood
hotspot. Menus offer a mix of Nordic classics and more modern
dishes; four per person is ample.

BOKBACKA 🍴

MODERN CUISINE • FASHIONABLE •
NEIGHBOURHOOD

XX ⇔

Skovveien 15 ✉ 0257 PLAN: A2
TEL. 412 60 144 – **www**.bokbacka.no
Closed Sunday and Monday
Menu 795 NOK (dinner only)

A unique 'food bar' with clean, light styling and fun, idiosyncratic
features; seats are arranged around the open kitchen, with only 4
other tables. Many of the theatrically presented dishes on the set
omakase-style menu have a story.

BRASSERIE BLANCHE ⅋○

FRENCH • COSY • BRASSERIE

Josefinesgate 23 ✉ 0352 **PLAN: B1**
TEL. 23 20 13 10 – **www**.blanche.no
Closed 3 weeks July, 24 December and Monday

Menu 495 NOK – Carte 339/599 NOK (dinner only)

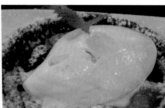

Cosy French restaurant housed in an 18C building, which was originally a stable and later spent time as a garage and an interior furnishings store. It has a small front terrace, a bar decorated with wine boxes and a wall made of corks. The chef is a Francophile and creates flavoursome classic French dishes.

BRASSERIE FRANCE ⅋○

FRENCH • BRASSERIE • TRADITIONAL DÉCOR

Øvre Slottsgate 16 ✉ 0157 **PLAN: C2**
Ⓜ Stortinget
TEL. 23 10 01 65 – **www**.brasseriefrance.no
Closed Easter, 23 December-2 January, Sunday and lunch Monday

Menu 320/395 NOK – Carte 470/660 NOK

A lively Gallic brasserie in a pedestrianised shopping street, with several private dining rooms. Brasserie classics from bouillabaisse to steak frites feature; for dessert, choose from the 'eat-as-much-as-you-like' pastry trolley.

CENTRE

BRASSERIE HANSKEN 🍴

MODERN CUISINE • FAMILY • BRASSERIE

Akersgate 2 ✉ 0158 PLAN: C2
Ⓜ Stortinget
TEL. 22 42 60 88 – **www**.brasseriehansken.no
Closed 3 weeks late July-early August, 1 week Easter, 1 week Christmas and Sunday
Menu 395/595 NOK – Carte 395/695 NOK

A delightfully traditional brasserie, centrally located by City Hall, with various charming dining areas and a fantastic terrace. Classical cooking follows the seasons and mixes French and Scandic influences; ingredients are top quality.

BRASSERIE PALEO 🍴

SCANDINAVIAN • TRENDY • TRENDY

Hotel Rosenkrantz • Rosenkrantz gate 1 ✉ 0159 PLAN: C2
Ⓜ National Theatrer
TEL. 23 31 55 80 – **www**.brasseriepaleo.no
Closed Christmas, Easter and July
Menu 185/495 NOK – Carte 495/605 NOK

With a name which reflects its philosophy, and a contemporary urban style, this is not your typical hotel restaurant. Watch the chefs prepare attractive modern Scandinavian dishes in the open kitchen. Service is professional and friendly.

CRU ⭐🍴

NORWEGIAN • WINE BAR • TRENDY   ✗ 🐝

Ingelbrecht, Knudssønsgt 1 ✉ 0265 PLAN: B1
TEL. 23 98 98 98 – **www**.cru.no
Closed July, 23 December-5 January and Sunday
Menu 545/495 NOK – Carte 457/507 NOK (dinner only)

Upstairs in the rustic restaurant they serve a set 4 course menu, with inventive British touches and 4 optional extra courses; downstairs in the more informal wine bar you can enjoy everything from nibbles through to a full à la carte menu.

DINNER 🍴

CHINESE • DESIGN • ELEGANT   ✗✗ Ⓐ🄲 ✜

Stortingsgata 22 ✉ 0161 PLAN: C2
Ⓜ National Theatret
TEL. 23 10 04 66 – **www**.dinner.no
Closed Christmas, Easter and Sunday lunch
Menu 258/499 NOK – Carte 365/1037 NOK

An intimate restaurant on the central square, close to the National Theatre. A black frosted glass façade masks a smart split-level interior. The kitchen focuses on Sichuan cuisine, with some artfully presented dim sum at lunch.

EKEBERG ⅏○

SEAFOOD • VINTAGE • DESIGN

Kongsveien 15 (Southeast: 1 km by Rostockergata, Bispegata amd Geitabru) ⊠ 0193
TEL. 23 24 23 00 – **www**.ekebergrestauranten.com
Closed Christmas
Menu 350/470 NOK – Carte 464/649 NOK

A delightfully restored art deco house on the hillside, with charming original fittings, several large terraces and commanding views over the fjords and the city. Cooking is careful, fresh and seasonal; seafood features highly.

FEINSCHMECKER ⅏○

TRADITIONAL CUISINE • CLASSIC DÉCOR • NEIGHBOURHOOD

Balchensgate 5 ⊠ 0265 **PLAN: A2**
TEL. 22 12 93 80 – **www**.feinschmecker.no
Closed 4 weeks summer, Easter, Christmas and Sunday
Menu 875 NOK – Carte 725/915 NOK (dinner only)

This long-standing restaurant has a cosy, welcoming atmosphere and a loyal local following, and is run by a charming team. The well-presented dishes are classically based, with French influences. Wine pairings are available.

FESTNINGEN 🍴○

MODERN CUISINE • BRASSERIE •
FASHIONABLE

XX 🦞 ⟨ ♿ 🏠 A/C 🍴 ▢

Myntgata 9 ✉ 0151 PLAN: C3
TEL. 22 83 31 00 – **www**.festningenrestaurant.no
Closed 19 December-6 January except dinner 31 December, 1 week
Easter and Sunday
Menu 315/595 NOK – Carte 615/705 NOK

A smart, contemporary brasserie with a terrace and lovely views
over the water to Aker Brygge; it was once a prison and its name
means 'fortress'. The experienced kitchen create unfussy, attractively
presented modern Nordic dishes using fresh local produce. The
impressive wine list is strong on Burgundy.

FJORD 🍴○

SEAFOOD • DESIGN • FASHIONABLE

XX A/C

Kristian Augusts Gt. 11 ✉ 0164 PLAN: C2
Ⓜ National Theatret
TEL. 22 98 21 50 (booking essential) – **www**.restaurantfjord.no
Closed Christmas, Easter, Sunday and Monday except in December
Menu 445/695 NOK (dinner only) (tasting menu only)

A contemporary restaurant opposite the National Gallery. Inside
it's dimly lit, with an open kitchen, unusual cobalt blue walls and
buffalo horns set into the chandeliers. The 3-5 course menu offers
flavoursome seafood dishes.

FRU K 🍴

MODERN CUISINE · DESIGN · FASHIONABLE ✕✕ ♿ A/C 🚗

Thief Hotel · Landgangen 1 ✉ 0252 **PLAN: B3**
TEL. 24 00 40 40 – **www**.thethief.com
Closed Easter, July, Christmas and Sunday
Menu 895/1095 NOK (dinner only) (tasting menu only)

Chic hotel restaurant, named after Fru Krogh, who tended animals on the Tjuvholmen peninsula long ago. Set 5 and 7 course menus use fine Norwegian ingredients to create tasty dishes. Take in the view from the rooftop 'Foodbar' in summer.

GAMLE RAADHUS 🍴

TRADITIONAL CUISINE · RUSTIC · ELEGANT ✕✕ 🏠

Nedre Slottsgate 1 ✉ 0151 **PLAN: C3**
Ⓜ Stortinget
TEL. 22 42 01 07 – **www**.gamle-raadhus.no
Closed 3 weeks July, 22 December-3 January, Easter and Sunday
Menu 425/469 NOK – Carte 510/705 NOK

Brightly painted house dating from 1641; its charming, antique-filled interior includes a library and an open-fired lounge. Lunch is served in the bar and classical dinners in the traditional dining room. There's also a lovely terrace.

HAPPOLATI ⽷

ASIAN • DESIGN • FRIENDLY

St. Olavs Plass 2 ✉ 0165 PLAN: C1
Ⓜ National Theatret
TEL. 479 78 087 – **www**.happolati.no
Closed Christmas and Easter
Menu 475/650 NOK – Carte 430/600 NOK

This bright, modish restaurant fuses Asian and Nordic styles; its assured cooking uses good quality ingredients and many dishes are designed for sharing. Tightly packed tables and friendly service add to the vibrant ambience.

HOS THEA ⽷

ITALIAN • FAMILY • NEIGHBOURHOOD

Gabelsgate 11 ✉ 0272 **PLAN: A2**
TEL. 22 44 68 74 – **www**.hosthea.no
Closed July, Christmas and Easter
Menu 545 NOK – Carte 665/690 NOK (dinner only)

A small, well-established restaurant in a charming residential area. It's decorated in natural hues and hung with beautiful oils. Menus offer a concise selection of Mediterranean dishes; start with the delicious homemade bread.

LOFOTEN FISKERESTAURANT ⅱO

SEAFOOD • BRASSERIE • SIMPLE

Stranden 75 ⊠ 0250 **PLAN: B3**
TEL. 22 83 08 08 – **www**.lofotenfiskerestaurant.no
Closed Christmas
Menu 345/550 NOK – Carte 410/705 NOK

A traditional fjord-side restaurant decorated in bright maritime colours and offering lovely views from its large windows and charming terrace. Watch as fresh, simply cooked fish and shellfish are prepared in the semi-open kitchen.

MARES ⅱO

FRENCH • NEIGHBOURHOOD • BRASSERIE

Skovveien 1 ⊠ 0257 **PLAN: A2**
TEL. 22 54 89 80 (booking advisable) – **www**.mares.no
Closed 12-18 April, 3 July-2 August, 23 December-3 January and Sunday
Menu 485 NOK – Carte 485/705 NOK (dinner only)

Neighbourhood restaurant with an adjoining deli and fish shop; it's bright and modern, with white furniture and a slightly industrial feel. Classical French menus have Spanish and Italian touches – order the fruits de mer 24hrs ahead.

NODEE BARCODE 🍴○

ASIAN • FASHIONABLE • TRENDY   ✗✗ 🏠 [A/C] ⇔

Dronning Eufemais Gate 28 ✉ 0191 PLAN: D3
Ⓜ Jernbanetorget
TEL. 22 93 34 50 – **www**.nodee.no
Closed Christmas, Easter and Sunday lunch
Menu 240/645 NOK – Carte 345/530 NOK

A moody, elegant ground floor restaurant serving an all-encompassing
Asian menu featuring dim sum, sushi and dishes cooked on the Robata
grill. There's a bar and terrace on the 13th floor and on the 14th floor
is Nodee Sky, with its appealing set menu and city views.

PLAH 🍴○

THAI • NEIGHBOURHOOD • FRIENDLY   ✗✗ 🏠 [A/C] ⇔

Hegdehaugsveien 22 ✉ 0167 PLAN: B1
TEL. 22 56 43 00 – **www**.plah.no
Closed 2 weeks July, Christmas, Easter and Sunday
Menu 695 NOK – Carte 525/695 NOK (dinner only)

Well-run restaurant offering tasty Thai dishes; Plah means 'fish' and
the produce is from local waters. The tasting and wine menus are
good value and service is knowledgeable. Their next door bar, Ahaan,
serves authentic street food.

STATHOLDERENS MAT OG VIN KJELLER ⁑◯

NORWEGIAN • RUSTIC • SIMPLE ✗

Statholdergaarden • Rådhusgate 11 (entrance from
Kirkegata) ⊠ 0151 PLAN: C3 – Ⓜ Stortinget
TEL. 22 41 88 00 (booking essential) – **www**.statholdergaarden.no
Closed 9 July-7 August, 23 December-3 January, 19-28 March, 1, 5
and 14-17 May, Sunday and Monday
Menu 695 NOK – Carte 660/680 NOK (dinner only)

The informal sister of Statholdergaarden – set over three rooms in
the old vaults beneath it. One wall of the large entranceway is filled
with wine bottles. Choose from a huge array of small plates or go for
the 10 course tasting menu.

THEATERCAFÉEN ⁑◯

TRADITIONAL CUISINE • LUXURY •
ROMANTIC   ✗✗ 🕸 ♿ 🆎 ⇗

Continental Hotel • Stortingsgaten 24-26 ⊠ 0117 PLAN: C2
Ⓜ National Theatret
TEL. 22 82 40 50 – **www**.theatercafeen.no
Closed Christmas, Easter and July
Menu 345/655 NOK – Carte 495/745 NOK

A prestigious Oslo institution in a grand hotel, this charming Viennese
'grand café' comes with pillars, black banquettes and art nouveau
lighting. Fresh cakes and elaborate lunchtime sandwiches make way
for ambitious dinners.

TJUVHOLMEN SJØMAGASINET ⅼO

SEAFOOD • DESIGN • BRASSERIE

Tjuvholmen Allé 14 ✉ 0251 **PLAN: B3**
TEL. 23 89 77 77 – **www**.sjomagasinet.no
Closed Christmas, Easter and Sunday
Menu 355/655 NOK – Carte 565/835 NOK

Vast restaurant with three dining rooms, a crab and lobster tank, a
superb terrace and a wet fish shop. Its name means 'sea store' and
menus are fittingly seafood based. Shellfish is from the nearby dock
– the langoustines are fantastic.

VAAGHALS ⅼO

SCANDINAVIAN • BRASSERIE •
FASHIONABLE

Dronning Eufemias gate 8 (Radhusgaten 30) ✉ 0151 **PLAN: D3**
Ⓜ Jernbanetorget
TEL. 920 70 999 – **www**.vaaghals.com
Closed 3 last weeks July, 22 December-3 January,
Easter and Sunday
Menu 650 NOK (dinner) – Carte 455/560 NOK

A bright, contemporary restaurant with an open kitchen and a terrace,
located on the ground floor of one of the modern 'barcode' buildings.
Scandinavian menus feature dry-aged meat; many of the dinner
dishes are designed for sharing.

CONTINENTAL

GRAND LUXURY • TRADITIONAL • CLASSIC

Stortingsgaten 24-26 ✉ 0117 PLAN: C2
Ⓜ National Theatret
TEL. 22 82 40 91 – www.hotelcontinental.no
Closed Christmas
155 rm ⌷ – ♦ 1695/3660 NOK ♦♦ 2295/4060 NOK – 3 suites
THEATERCAFÉEN – See restaurant listing

A classic hotel situated by the National Theatre and run by the 4th generation of the family, who ensure the service remains very personal. Bedrooms are stylish and contemporary – Deluxe are spacious and come with bathrobes and sofas. Dine in the grand café or from an inventive daily menu in Annen Etage.

GRAND

GRAND LUXURY • TRADITIONAL • CLASSIC

Karl Johans Gate 31 ✉ 0159 PLAN: C2
Ⓜ Stortinget
TEL. 23 21 20 00 – www.grand.no
292 rm ⌷ – ♦ 1550/3100 NOK ♦♦ 1550/3100 NOK – 7 suites

An imposing, centrally located hotel built in 1874; the guest areas and grand ballrooms reflect this. Bedrooms are charming: some are modern, some are feminine and others are in a belle époque style. The winners of the Nobel Prize are interviewed here! International fare in elegant Palmen. Nordic-inspired cooking in the Grand Café.

CENTRE

CENTRE

RADISSON BLU PLAZA

BUSINESS • MODERN • FUNCTIONAL

Sonja Henies Plass 3 ✉ 0134 PLAN: D2
Ⓜ Jernbanetorget
TEL. 22 05 80 00 – **www**.radissonblu.com/plazahotel-oslo
676 rm ⌕ – 🛉 1195/5745 NOK 🛉🛉 1395/5945 NOK – 19 suites

This is Norway's tallest hotel and it boasts more bedrooms than any other in Oslo; the modern 'Business' rooms are the most comfortable. It has a large marble lobby with a lounge and bar, extensive conference facilities, an Irish pub and a top floor restaurant offering a Norwegian menu and city views.

CLARION COLLECTION H. BASTION

BUSINESS • MODERN

Skippergata 7 ✉ 0152 PLAN: C3
Ⓜ Jernbanetorget
TEL. 22 47 77 00 – **www**.choicehotels.no
Closed Easter and Christmas
99 rm ⌕ – 🛉 1460/2980 NOK 🛉🛉 1460/3180 NOK – 5 suites

Set on the edge of the city, close to the port, this hotel has friendly staff, a cosy lounge and a charming English-style lobby which offers free snacks. Bedrooms vary in both their size and furnishings; many have seating areas.

CLARION COLLECTION H. GABELSHUS

TRADITIONAL • BUSINESS • CLASSIC

Gabelsgate 16 ✉ 0272 PLAN: A2
TEL. 23 27 65 00 – **www**.nordicchoicehotels.no
Closed Easter and Christmas
114 rm ☲ – 🛏 800/2240 NOK 🛏🛏 940/2780 NOK – 1 suite

Beautiful ivy-covered house with a peaceful atmosphere, in a smart residential neighbourhood. The classical wood-furnished lounge has a complimentary all-day buffet. Charming bedrooms offer a pleasing contrast between old and new.

COMFORT H. GRAND CENTRAL

CHAIN • BUSINESS • FUNCTIONAL

Jernbanetorget 1 ✉ 0154 PLAN: D2
🚇 Jernbanetorget
TEL. 22 98 28 00 – **www**.comfortgrandcentral.no
170 rm ☲ – 🛏 1420/1949 NOK 🛏🛏 1610/2249 NOK

A great choice for businesspeople, this delightful hotel has a superb location above the main train station. 130 of the soundproofed bedrooms have been individually styled and boast coordinating fabrics and colour schemes, as well as feature bathrooms. The restaurant offers a menu of simple Italian dishes.

OPERA

BUSINESS • MODERN

Dronning Eufemias gate 4 ✉ 0191 PLAN: D2
Ⓜ Jernbanetorget
TEL. 24 10 30 00 – www.thonhotels.no/opera
Closed 24-31 December
480 rm 🛏 – 🛉 1095/2655 NOK 🛉🛉 1195/2755 NOK – 2 suites

Imposing light-stone building in front of the Opera House, close to
the sea. Guest areas are spacious; bedrooms are a split of classic
and modern styles but all are equally well-equipped. The restaurant
boasts huge windows and panoramic views; watch the chefs at work
in the open kitchen.

ROSENKRANTZ

BUSINESS • CHAIN • FUNCTIONAL

Rosenkrantz gate 1 ✉ 0159 PLAN: C2
Ⓜ National Theatret
TEL. 23 31 55 00 – www.thonhotels.no
151 rm 🛏 – 🛉 1145/2895 NOK 🛉🛉 1445/4095 NOK
BRASSERIE PALEO – See restaurant listing

Located in the city centre and perfect for the business traveller. The
brightly styled 8th floor guest lounge has complimentary coffee,
mineral water, fruit and cakes. Functional bedrooms come with Smart
TVs and modern bathrooms.

THIEF

LUXURY • CONTEMPORARY

🏋 ♿ 💯 ⚕ AC 🦽 🚗

Landgangen 1 ✉ 0252 PLAN: B3
TEL. 24 00 40 00 – **www**.thethief.com
116 rm ☕ – 🛉 2290/4290 NOK 🛉🛉 2590/4590 NOK – 9 suites
FRU K – See restaurant listing

A smart hotel with a superb spa, located on a huge development on Thief Island. Works from global artists – including Andy Warhol – feature throughout; facilities are state-of-the-art and a tablet controls all of the technology in the bedrooms.

CLARION COLLECTION H. SAVOY

BUSINESS • CLASSIC

🏋 ⚕

Universitetsgata 11 ✉ 0164 PLAN: C2 Ⓜ National Theatret
TEL. 23 35 42 00 – **www**.nordicchoicehotels.no
Closed 20-27 December and Easter
93 rm ☕ – 🛉 940/2440 NOK 🛉🛉 1036/2680 NOK

RESTAURANT EIK ⊕ – See restaurant listing

Centrally located by the National Gallery, in a building dating back to 1850. Bedrooms are decorated in a mix of classic and more contemporary styles; the latter feature 'action photos'. They offer complimentary breakfasts and light meals.

PARK INN

BUSINESS • CHAIN • FUNCTIONAL

 ♿ AC

Ovre Slottsgate 2c ⊠ 0157 PLAN: C2
Ⓜ Stortinget
TEL. 22 40 01 00 – **www**.parkinn.com/hotel-oslo
118 rm ☕ – 👤 995/3295 NOK 👥 1095/3395 NOK

A converted apartment block near Karl Johans Gate. Inside it's bright and modern with pleasant guest areas. Good-sized, functional bedrooms have pale wood furniture and modern lighting; the top floor rooms have balconies.

SAGA H. OSLO

TOWNHOUSE • HISTORIC • GRAND LUXURY

  P

Eilert Sundstgate 39 ⊠ 0259 PLAN: B1
TEL. 22 55 44 90 – **www**.sagahoteloslo.no
Closed Christmas and Easter
47 rm ☕ – 👤 995/2895 NOK 👥 1095/3495 NOK

A late Victorian townhouse with a smart, contemporary interior, set in a quiet city suburb. Most of the bedrooms are spacious: they have bold feature walls, modern facilities – including coffee machines – and small but stylish shower rooms. There's a Japanese restaurant in the basement.

SCANDIC VULKAN

BUSINESS • CHAIN • DESIGN

Maridalsveien 13 ⊠ 0178 PLAN: D1
TEL. 2105 7100 – **www**.scandichotels.com/vulkan
Closed Christmas and Easter
149 rm ☑ – ♦ 830/1900 NOK ♦♦ 1050/2350 NOK

A designer hotel on the site of a former silver mine, next to a great food market. Modern bedrooms have bold feature walls and good facilities; the external-facing ones have full length windows. The bright, informal restaurant offers an Italian-influenced menu, and adjoins a trendy bar and deli.

SPECTRUM

BUSINESS • FUNCTIONAL

Brugata 7 ⊠ 0186 PLAN: D2
Ⓜ Grønland
TEL. 23 36 27 00 – **www**.thonhotels.no/spectrum
Closed Christmas
151 rm ☑ – ♦ 1575/1875 NOK ♦♦ 1750/2075 NOK

Good value lodge-style hotel in a pedestrianised shopping street, close to the station. An unassuming exterior conceals a modern lobby and a spacious breakfast room. Light-hued bedrooms offer basic comforts; some sleep up to four.

VIKA ATRIUM

CONFERENCE HOTEL • FUNCTIONAL

𝌎 ⌘ ⇆ ♨ 🚗

Munkedamsveien 45 ✉ 0250 PLAN: B2
Ⓜ National Theatret
TEL. 22 83 33 00 – **www**.thonhotels.no
102 rm ☕ – 🛇 999/2045 NOK 🛇🛇 1195/2695 NOK

A busy conference hotel located in a large modern office block in the redeveloped harbour area. Functional bedrooms are set over 7 floors and have contemporary styling and marble bathrooms: some overlook the atrium, others the street.

GREFSENKOLLEN 🍴

NORWEGIAN • ROMANTIC • COSY   XX ⪡ 🛖 ⇮

Grefsenkollveien 100 (North: 10 km by Ring 3) ✉ 0490
TEL. 22 79 70 60 (booking essential at dinner) –
www.grefsenkollen.no
Closed July, Christmas and dinner Sunday-Monday and Easter
Menu 250/845 NOK – Carte lunch 420/600 NOK

A fairytale chalet in the mountains, with a spacious terrace, a characterful open-fired dining room and lovely views over the city and fjord. Appealing 3 and 5 course dinner menus are well-balanced, intricate and playful – Norwegian ingredients take centre stage. Lunch is light; dinner offers wine pairings.

CLARION OSLO AIRPORT

BUSINESS • FUNCTIONAL

Hans Gaarderveg 15 (Northeast: 45 km by E 6) ✉ 2060
TEL. 63 94 94 94 – **www**.clarionosloairport.no
432 rm ⌂ – ∮ 1145/1335 NOK ∮∮ 1145/1335 NOK

Typical two-storey Norwegian house, accessed from the airport by
a shuttle bus; it has one of the largest conference capacities in the
country. Modern Scandinavian bedrooms come in pale hues. Live
music features in the bar and open-fired lounges, and buffet meals
are served in the traditional restaurant.

DE FEM STUER ⱔ○

NORWEGIAN • ELEGANT • ROMANTIC XⱭX ⟨ 占 A/C ⟳ P

Holmenkollen Park Hotel • Kongeveien 26 (Northwest: 10 km by
Bogstadveien, Sørkedalsveien and Holmenkollveien) ✉ 0787
Ⓜ Holmenkollen
TEL. 22 92 27 34 – **www**.holmenkollenparkhotel.no
Closed 21 December-2 January

Menu 325/395 NOK – Carte 655/885 NOK

A series of five elegant dining rooms in an impressive hotel; three
with delightful 20C panelling. A buffet lunch is followed by a concise,
seasonal à la carte and a daily set menu. Cooking is classical and
displays French influences.

HOLMENKOLLEN PARK

TRADITIONAL • PERSONALISED

🐌 🐾 ♿ 🖼 💷 🎐 🛏 AC ✂ 🏊 🚗

ongeveien 26 (Northwest: 10 km by Bogstadveien, Sørkedalsveien nd Holmenkollveien) ⊠ 0787
Holmenkollen – TEL. 22 92 20 00 – **www**.holmenkollenparkhotel.no
osed 21 December-2 January
36 rm ☕ – ♦ 1049/2099 NOK ♦♦ 1049/2099 NOK
E FEM STUER – See restaurant listing

n impressive 1894 red wood building (once a sanatorium for TB atients!), located beside a world-class ski resort. The interior isplays a curious mix of styles, from the classical to the modern; hree of the bedrooms have their own saunas.

STRAND 🍴

CANDINAVIAN • TRADITIONAL DÉCOR • USTIC

XX 🪑 AC ⇔ 🅿

trandalleén 43 (Southwest: 9 km by E18) ⊠ 1368
EL. 67 53 05 75 – **www**.strandrestaurant.no
losed Christmas, Easter and Monday
Menu 175/625 NOK – Carte 465/625 NOK

An 18C wooden house with a bakery and café, set in a quiet seaside own. The restaurant is bright and contemporary with an open :itchen and a terrace affording views out over the marina. Classic Scandinavian cooking uses organic produce.

BEKKJARVIK GJESTGIVERI 🍴○

MODERN CUISINE • INN • CLASSIC DÉCOR ✕✕ ≤ P

Bekkjarvik Gjestgiveri Hotel • Bekkjarvik (Southwest: 14 km by Fv 546 and Fv 154) ✉ 5399
TEL. 55 08 42 40 (bookings essential for non-residents) – **www.**bekkjarvikgjestgiveri.no
Closed 23-26 December and 30 December-2 January
Carte 485/690 NOK

A traditionally furnished restaurant in a family-owned and run hotel; the son is the one behind the stove. Choose 2, 3 or 7 dishes from the menu. Classic cooking uses good quality ingredients and is delivered with a modern hand.

BEKKJARVIK GJESTGIVERI 🏠

TRADITIONAL • RURAL
≤ 🏡 🏖 P

Bekkjarvik (Southwest: 14 km by Fv 546 and Fv 154) ✉ 5399
TEL. 55 08 42 41 – **www.**bekkjarvikgjestgiveri.no
Closed 23-26 December and 30 December-2 January
21 rm ☕ – 🛉 1590 NOK 🛉🛉 1790/3500 NOK
BEKKJARVIK GJESTGIVERI – See restaurant listing

Built by royal decree, this 17C hotel is delightfully located in a quiet fishing port on the south of the island. Comfy, simply furnished bedrooms are split between the original building and an annexe; the latter have lovely harbour views.

LYSVERKET ⭐🍽️

MODERN CUISINE • DESIGN • FASHIONABLE   XX 🅰🅲 ⇔

Rasmus Meyers Allé 9 ✉ 5015
TEL. 55 60 3100 – **www**.lysverket.no
Closed 23 December-2 January, Easter lunch, Monday dinner and
Sunday
Menu 695 NOK, 995/995 NOK (dinner) – Carte lunch 335/735 NOK

This spacious, stylish restaurant is situated in a 1930s art museum
overlooking the park and offers an à la carte lunch and a set dinner
menu of 4 or 7 courses. Original modern dishes are made with quality
local ingredients.

RE-NAA ✿

CREATIVE • INTIMATE • ELEGANT   XX

Steinkargata 10 (Breitorget) ✉ 4006
TEL. 51 55 11 11 (booking essential) – **www**.restaurantrenaa.no
Closed Easter, mid July-mid August, 22 December-4 January,
Sunday and Monday
Menu 1400 NOK (dinner only) (tasting menu only)

Chef:
Sven Erik Renaa
Specialities:
Cod with onion and caviar. Suckling
lamb in two servings. Rhubarb with
tarragon.

An appealing timber house in the quaint streets of the old town;
the elegant restaurant has just 7 tables and an open kitchen at its
centre. The experienced chef-owner offers a lengthy set menu of up
to 20 courses which are a modern take on classic French cooking.
Ingredients are exceptional and their preparation precise; flavours
are distinct and superbly balanced.

SABI OMAKASE ❀

SUSHI • INTIMATE • FRIENDLY

XX

Pedersgata 38 ✉ 4013
TEL. 925 43 781 (booking essential) – **www**.omakase.no
Closed Sunday-Wednesday
Menu 1295 NOK (dinner only) (tasting menu only)

Chef:
Roger Asakil Joya
Specialities:
Squid with lime and yuzu. Venison
with sea salt. Sesame ice cream
with sake-marinated melon.

Sit at one of the nine seats at the counter to enjoy an 18 course
sushi experience, with each course introduced and explained by the
experienced chef-owner. Superlative Norwegian ingredients are
prepared with exceptional skill and embellished with subtle modern
touches. Sake or wine pairings accompany.

TANGO BAR & KJØKKEN ⑩

MODERN CUISINE • SIMPLE

XX

Nedre Strandgate 25 ✉ 4005
TEL. 51 50 12 30 (booking essential) – **www**.tango-bk.no
Closed Christmas-New Year, Easter, Sunday and bank holidays
Menu 395/995 NOK (dinner only and Saturday lunch) (tasting menu
only)

Pleasantly located by the quayside, this smart restaurant is dominated
by its open kitchen. The 3 course set menu offers a subtle modern
interpretation of classic cooking and dishes are founded on good
ingredients and sound techniques.

CREDO 🍴

CREATIVE • INTIMATE   XX [A/C]

Ørjveita 4 ✉ 7010
TEL. 73 53 03 88 (booking essential) – **www**.restaurantcredo.no
Closed Sunday and Monday
Menu 950 NOK (dinner only) (tasting menu only)

A surprise 3-5 course menu of accomplished, modern cooking is
served at this simply furnished restaurant with its long open kitchen.
Dishes have a subtle lightness and a pleasing originality and service
is professional yet relaxed.

E. Berthier/hemis.fr

SWEDEN

AWARDS

✿ ✿

Oaxen Krog	STOCKHOLM	203
Vollmers	MALMÖ	242
Fäviken Magasinet	JÄRPEN	256

✿

Ekstedt	STOCKHOLM	172
Esperanto	STOCKHOLM	172
Gastrologik	STOCKHOLM	173
Imouto	STOCKHOLM	173
Mathias Dahlgren-Matbaren	STOCKHOLM	174
Operakällaren	STOCKHOLM	174
Sushi Sho	STOCKHOLM	175
Volt	STOCKHOLM	175
Bhoga	GOTHENBURG	218
Koka	GOTHENBURG	218
Sjömagasinet	GOTHENBURG	219
SK Mat & Människor	GOTHENBURG	219
Thörnströms Kök	GOTHENBURG	220
28+	GOTHENBURG	220
Upper House	GOTHENBURG	221
Bloom in the Park	MALMÖ	243
Sture	MALMÖ	243
Hotell Borgholm	ÖLAND	256
Daniel Berlin	SKÅNE TRANÅS	257
PM & Vänner	VÄXJÖ	258

😊

Brasserie Bobonne	STOCKHOLM	176
Den Gyldene Freden	STOCKHOLM	200
EAT	STOCKHOLM	176
Lilla Ego	STOCKHOLM	177
Nook	STOCKHOLM	206
Oaxen Slip	STOCKHOLM	204
Proviant Östermalm	STOCKHOLM	177
Rolfs Kök	STOCKHOLM	178
Ulla Winbladh	STOCKHOLM	204
Familjen	GOTHENBURG	221
Somm	GOTHENBURG	222
Bastard	MALMÖ	244
Cirkus at More Bistro	MALMÖ	244
Namu	MALMÖ	245

STOCKHOLM

Sweden

A. Saffo/Sime/Photononstop

Stockholm is the place to go for clean air, big skies and handsome architecture. And water. One of the great beauties of the city is the amount of water that runs through and around it; it's built on 14 islands, and looks out on 24,000 of them. An astounding two-thirds of the area within the city limits is made up of water, parks and woodland, and there are dozens of little bridges to cross to get from one part of town to another. It's little wonder Swedes appear so calm and relaxed. It's in Stockholm that the salty waters of the Baltic meet head-on the fresh waters of Lake Mälaren, reflecting the broad boulevards and

elegant buildings that shimmer along their edge. Domes, spires and turrets dot a skyline that in the summertime never truly darkens. The heart of the city is the Old Town, Gamla Stan, full of alleyways and lanes little changed from their medieval origins. Just to the north is the modern centre, Norrmalm: a buzzing quarter of shopping malls, restaurants and bars. East of Gamla Stan you reach the small island of Skeppsholmen, which boasts fine views of the waterfront; directly north from here is Östermalm, an area full of grand residences, while southeast you'll find the lovely park island of Djurgården. South and west of Gamla Stan are the two areas where Stockholmers particularly like to hang out, the trendy (and hilly) Södermalm, and Kungsholmen.

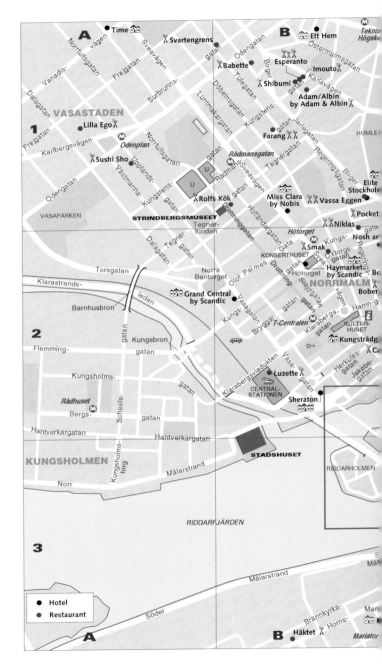

A
Time
Svartengrens
Babette
Esperanto
Imouto
Shibumi
Adam/Albin
by Adam & Albin

VASASTADEN
Lilla Ego
Odenplan
Sushi Sho
Farang

Rådmansgatan
Rolfs Kök
Miss Clara
by Nobis
Vassa Eggen
Pocket

STRINDBERGSMUSEET
Tegnér-
lunden
Niklas
Hötorget
Smak
Nosh ar
KONSERTHUSET
Haymarket
by Scandic
NORRMALM
Bober

Torsgatan
Norra
Bantorget
Grand Central
by Scandic

Klarastrands-
leden
Barnhusbron
T-Centralen
KULTUR-
HUSET
Kungsträdg

2
Kungsbron
Flemming-
gatan
Kungsholms-
Luzette
Rådhuset
CENTRAL-
STATIONEN
Bergs-
Sheraton
Hantverkargatan
Hantverkargatan
KUNGSHOLMEN
STADSHUSET
Norr
Mälarstrand
RIDDARHOLMEN

RIDDARFJÄRDEN

3
Mälarstrand
Söder
Brännkyrka-
Horns-

● Hotel
● Restaurant

A
B Häktet
Mariator

B Ett Hem
Teknis
Högsko
Östermalmsgatan
Odengatan
Karlavägen
HUMLE
Elite
Stockho

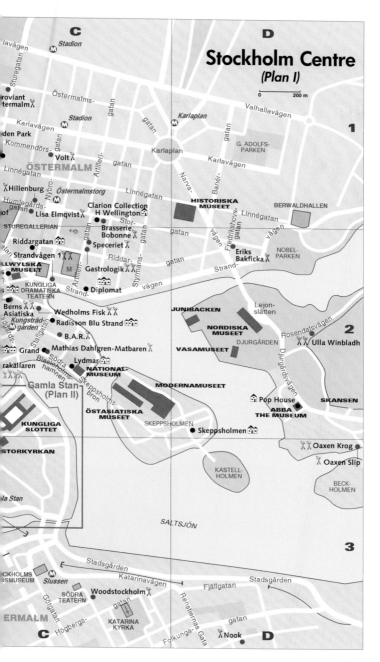

Stockholm Centre
(Plan I)

0   200 m

C   Stadion
Stadion
Karlaplan
Karlaplan
Valhallavägen
G. ADOLFS-PARKEN
BERWALDHALLEN

Sturegatan
lavägen
roviant
termalm
Karlavägen
den Park
Kommendörs-
Volt
Linnégatan
ÖSTERMALM

Hillenburg
Östermalmstorg
Lisa Elmqvist
Humlegårds-
gatan
of
STUREGALLERIAN
Riddargatan
Strandvägen 1
LLWYLSKA
MUSEET
KUNGLIGA
DRAMATISKA
TEATERN
Berns
Asiatiska
Kungsträd-
gården
Grand
rakällaren
Gamla Stan
(Plan II)

KUNGLIGA
SLOTTET
STORKYRKAN
la Stan

Östermalms-
Artilleri-
gatan
Linnégatan
Clarion Collection
H Wellington
Stor-
Brasserie
Bobonne
Speceriet
Riddar-
Gastrologik
Diplomat
Wedholms Fisk
Radisson Blu Strand
B.A.R.
Mathias Dahlgren-Matbaren
Lydmar
NATIONAL-MUSEUM
Södra
Blasieholms-
hammen
Skeppsholms-
bron
ÖSTASIATISKA
MUSEET

Nybro-
Styrmans-
vägen
Riddar-
gatan
Strand-
Strand-

HISTORISKA
MUSEET
Navra-
Banér-
Fredrikshovs-
gatan
Linnégatan
Eriks
Bakficka
NOBEL-PARKEN

JUNIBACKEN
NORDISKA
MUSEET
DJURGÅRDEN
VASAMUSEET
Lejon-slätten
Rosendalsvägen
Ulla Winbladh
Djurgårdsvägen

MODERNAMUSEET
Pop House
ABBA
THE MUSEUM
SKANSEN
SKEPPSHOLMEN
Skeppsholmen

KASTELL-HOLMEN
Oaxen Krog
Oaxen Slip
BECK-HOLMEN

SALTSJÖN

Stadsgården
Katarinavägen
Fjällgatan
Stadsgården
CKHOLMS
SMUSEUM
Slussen
SÖDRA
TEATERN
Woodstockholm
KATARINA
KYRKA
Renstiernas Gata
Folkunga-Gata
ERMALM
Högbergs-
Götgatan
Nook
C   D

EKSTEDT ✿

MEATS AND GRILLS • DESIGN • FRIENDLY   ✗ 🌼 ⚐

Humlegårdsgatan 17 ✉ 114 46 PLAN: C1
Ⓜ Östermalmstorg
TEL. 08-611 12 10 (booking essential) – **www**.ekstedt.nu
Closed last 2 weeks July, Christmas-New Year, Sunday and Monday
Menu 840/1090 SEK (dinner only) (tasting menu only)

Specialities:
Blackened leeks with vendace
roe and charcoal-smoked cream.
Pike-perch with chanterelles and
peas. Wood-fired honey cake with
raspberries.

An unassuming façade hides a very relaxed, friendly, yet professionally
run brasserie, where ingredients are cooked in a wood-burning
oven, over a fire-pit or smoked through a chimney using birch wood.
Dishes are inventive but well-balanced – they are given their finishing
touches at the stone bar.

ESPERANTO ✿

CREATIVE • FASHIONABLE • DESIGN   ✗✗✗ A/C

Kungstensgatan 2 (1st Floor) ✉ 114 25 PLAN: B1
Ⓜ Tekniska Högskolan
TEL. 08-696 23 23 – **www**.esperantorestaurant.se
Closed Christmas-New Year, Easter, July and Sunday-Tuesday
Menu 1400/1850 SEK (dinner only) (tasting menu only)

Chef:
Sayan Isaksson
Specialities:
Silk tofu, buckwheat and langoustine.
Pressed beef marrow, potato water
and caviar. Blueberry, milk and
horseradish.

'Esperanto' is a language that crosses frontiers, and the food here has
an equally universal feel. Passionately prepared, original Swedish and
Asian dishes feature a great range of ingredients and have a theatrical
element – which is fitting seeing as the restaurant is on the first floor
of an old theatre. In one corner there's a small sushi counter.

GASTROLOGIK ✿

WORLD CUISINE • INTIMATE • DESIGN

XX ✿

Artillerigatan 14 ✉ 114 51 PLAN: C2
Ⓜ Östermalmstorg
TEL. 08-662 30 60 (booking essential) – **www**.gastrologik.se
Closed Christmas, Sunday and Monday

Menu 1395 SEK (dinner only) (surprise menu only)

Chef:
Jacob Holmström and Anton Bjuhr
Specialities:
Algae-glazed asparagus with grilled butter. Reindeer with matsutake mushrooms and cabbage. Lovage ice cream, frozen sorrel juice and spruce tips.

This intimate restaurant is owned by two accomplished young chefs. Cooking is innovative, flavours are pure and each main ingredient is allowed to shine. Dishes rely on the latest seasonal ingredients to arrive at the door, so are constantly evolving; the menu isn't presented to you until the end of the meal.

IMOUTO ✿

SUSHI • INTIMATE • SIMPLE

X A/C

Kungstensgatan 2 (1st Floor) ✉ 114 25 PLAN: B1
Ⓜ Tekniska Högskolan
TEL. 08-696 23 23 (booking essential) – **www**.imouto.se
Closed Christmas-New Year, Easter, midsummer and Sunday-Tuesday

Menu 1200 SEK (dinner only)

Chef:
Sayan Isaksson
Specialities:
Soy-glazed langoustine. Turbot with wild garlic oil. Pike-perch sushi.

Its name means 'little sister' and you'll find this 9-seater sushi counter in the corner of Esperanto restaurant. Only an omakase menu is offered, with hot and cold dishes served before the sushi; the rice is from Japan but the fish is mainly from Swedish waters. There are two sittings on Fridays and Saturdays.

MATHIAS DAHLGREN-MATBAREN ❀

MODERN CUISINE • FASHIONABLE • DESIGN

Grand Hotel • Södra Blasieholmshamnen 6 ✉ 103 27 **PLAN: C2**
Ⓜ Kungsträdgården
TEL. 08-679 35 00 (booking advisable) – **www**.mdghs.com
Closed 14 July-8 August, 22 December-10 January,
Saturday lunch and Sunday
Carte 475/835 SEK

Specialities:
Scandinavian ceviche, horseradish, elderflower and algae. Seared pork, creamy corn and chilli. Baked chocolate, sour cream, toffee ice cream and nuts.

This popular hotel restaurant is both fun and charmingly run. The open kitchen specialises in flavoursome, well-balanced dishes from an appealing menu divided into the headings 'From our country', 'From other countries' or 'From the plant world'. They keep some seats at the counter for those who haven't booked.

OPERAKÄLLAREN ❀

CLASSIC CUISINE • CHIC • LUXURY

Operahuset, Karl XII's Torg ✉ 111 86 **PLAN: C2**
Ⓜ Kungsträdgården
TEL. 08-676 58 01 – **www**.operakallaren.se
Closed 7 July-7 August, 20-21 June, 25-30 December, 1-12 January,
Sunday and Monday
Menu 1050/1550 SEK (dinner only)

Specialities:
Mackerel with trout roe and browned butter. Saddle and cured fillet of lamb with artichoke cream. Peach with caramel bavarois and elderflower granité.

Sweden's most opulent restaurant sits within the historic Opera House, and the stunning, high-ceilinged room boasts original gilt panelling decorated with frescoes and carvings. Carefully constructed dishes are underpinned by classic techniques. The wine list boasts extensive vintages of the world's great wines.

SUSHI SHO ❀

JAPANESE • NEIGHBOURHOOD • FRIENDLY

Upplandsgatan 45 ⊠ 113 28 **PLAN: A1**
Ⓜ Odenplan
TEL. 08-30 30 30 – **www**.sushisho.se
Closed Christmas-New Year, July, midsummer, Sunday and Monday
Menu 595 SEK (dinner only)

Chef:
Carl Ishizaki
Specialities:
Soy-cured egg yolk with okra, tuna and toasted rice. Salmon, sea bass and scallop nigiri. Razor clam with edamame & pea purée, sake and ginger.

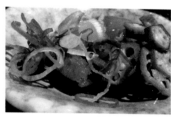

With its white, tiled walls and compact counter seating the room couldn't be simpler, but the food is sublime. Meals are served 'omakase' style, with the chef deciding what's best each day and dishes arriving as they're ready. Top quality seafood from local waters features alongside some great egg recipes.

VOLT ❀

CREATIVE • INTIMATE • NEIGHBOURHOOD

Kommendörsgatan 16 ⊠ 114 48 **PLAN: C1**
Ⓜ Stadion
TEL. 08-662 34 00 (booking essential) – **www**.restaurangvolt.se
Closed 4 weeks summer, Christmas, Sunday and Monday
Menu 585/765 SEK (dinner only)

Chef:
Peter Andersson and Fredrik Johnsson
Specialities:
Grilled beans, oysters and algae. Sweetbread, spring garlic and green strawberries. Blackcurrants and parsnip.

An intimate, welcoming restaurant run by a young but experienced team. Cooking is natural in style, with the largely organic produce yielding clear, bold flavours – natural wines also feature. Ingredients are arranged in layers, so that each forkful contains a little of everything; choose 4 or 6 courses.

BRASSERIE BOBONNE 😊

FRENCH • COSY • BISTRO

Storgatan 12 ✉ 114 44 **PLAN: C1**
Ⓜ Östermalmstorg
TEL. 08-660 03 18 (booking essential) – **www**.bobonne.se
Closed 5 weeks July-August, midsummer, Christmas, Easter,
Sunday and lunch Saturday
Menu 249/550 SEK – Carte 325/615 SEK

Sweet little two-roomed restaurant with comfy chairs, period floor
tiles and a homely feel. The open-plan kitchen fills the room with
pleasant aromas and the blackboard lists tasty, well-balanced dishes
crafted from fresh ingredients. Menus are French-inspired, with
modern touches and the odd Swedish influence.

EAT 😊

ASIAN • BRASSERIE • FASHIONABLE

Jakobsbergsgatan 15 ✉ 111 44 **PLAN: B2**
Ⓜ Hötorget
TEL. 08-509 203 00 (bookings advisable at dinner) –
www.eatrestaurant.se
Closed Christmas-New Year, lunch mid July-mid August,
Sunday and lunch Saturday
Menu 440 SEK – Carte 200/585 SEK

Pass the EAT 'Market' fast food outlet in this upmarket shopping mall
and head for the Oriental 'Bistro' with its rich, moody colour scheme
and central cocktail bar. The name stands for 'European Asian Taste'
and the Chinese dishes are flavoursome, well-executed and designed
for sharing. Opening times can vary.

LILLA EGO 🐸

MODERN CUISINE • FRIENDLY • SIMPLE ✗ 🍴

Västmannag 69 ✉ 113 26 PLAN: A1
Ⓜ Odenplan
TEL. 08-27 44 55 (booking essential) – **www**.lillaego.com
Closed Christmas, Easter, July Sunday and Monday
Carte 495/675 SEK (dinner only)

One of the hottest tickets in town comes with a pared-down look and a buzzy vibe; if you haven't booked, try for a counter seat. The two modest chef-owners have created an appealingly priced menu of robust, satisfying, seasonal dishes. The 'wrestling' sausage will challenge even the biggest of appetites.

PROVIANT ÖSTERMALM 🐸

SWEDISH • BISTRO • INTIMATE ✗ ⅙ ☂

Sturegatan 19 ✉ 114 36 PLAN: C1
Ⓜ Stadion
TEL. 08-22 60 50 – **www**.proviant.se
Closed 2 weeks Christmas-New Year, 3 weeks July, and lunch Saturday-Sunday
Menu 295/575 SEK – Carte 455/595 SEK

Lively restaurant boasting smart, contemporary décor, a small counter and an adjoining foodstore; located in a chic residential area by Sture Park. Swedish ingredients feature highly – choose from the rustic, classically based dishes on the blackboard, the French-inspired à la carte or the house specialities.

ROLFS KÖK 🐵

MODERN CUISINE • BISTRO • RUSTIC

Tegnérgatan 41 ⊠ 111 61 **PLAN: B1**
Ⓜ Rådmansgatan
TEL. 08-10 16 96 (booking essential) – **www**.rolfskok.se
Closed July, 24-26 December, midsummer and lunch Saturday-Sunday

Carte 415/700 SEK

A popular, buzzy restaurant in a lively commercial district, run by a passionate chef-owner. The contemporary interior was designed by famous Swedish artists; sit at the counter to watch the chefs in action. Dishes include homely Swedish classics and blackboard specials. Every dish has a wine match.

ADAM/ALBIN BY ADAM & ALBIN 🍴

MODERN CUISINE • INTIMATE • NEIGHBOURHOOD

Rådmansgatan 16 ⊠ 114 25 **PLAN: B1**
Ⓜ Tekniska Högskolan
TEL. 08-411 55 35 (booking essential) – **www**.adamalbin.se
Closed Sunday, bank holidays and restricted opening in summer

Menu 795 SEK (dinner only)

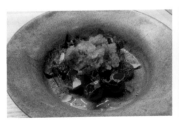

Stylish restaurant with Italian marble walls and a mix of individual and communal tables. Following a snack, there are two choices per course. Refined, eye-catching dishes blend the ethos of a Scandic kitchen with global flavours.

AG ⁙◯

MEATS AND GRILLS • RUSTIC • FASHIONABLE ✗✗ 🦂 AC

Kronobergsgatan 37 (2nd Floor), Kungsholmen
(via Flemminggatan) ✉ 112 33
Ⓜ Fridshemsplan
TEL. 08-410 68 100 – www.restaurangag.se
Closed July, 23-25 June, 24-26 December and Sunday
Carte 335/1285 SEK (dinner only)

An industrial, New York style eatery on the 2nd floor of an old silver
factory. Swedish, American and Scottish beef is displayed in huge
cabinets and you choose your accompaniments. Expect a great wine
list and smooth service.

B.A.R. ⁙◯

SEAFOOD • BRASSERIE • TRENDY ✗ AC

Blasieholmsgatan 4a ✉ 111 48 PLAN: C2
Ⓜ Kungsträdgården
TEL. 08-611 53 35 – www.restaurangbar.se
Closed Christmas-New Year, midsummer, lunch July and Sunday
Carte 395/800 SEK

Spacious, canteen-style restaurant with an industrial feel. The wide-
ranging menu changes with each season and offers some interesting
side dishes. For the daily specials, head to the counter and select your
meat or fish from the ice display.

BABETTE ⑩

MODERN CUISINE • NEIGHBOURHOOD • BISTRO

Roslagsgatan 6 ⊠ 113 55 **PLAN: B1**
Ⓜ Tekniska Högskolan
TEL. 08-509 022 24 – **www**.babette.se
Closed 24-26, 31 December and June 18-25

Carte 295/415 SEK (dinner only)

You'll feel at home in this modern neighbourhood bistro. Cooking is rustic and unfussy and the daily selection of small plates and pizzas makes dining flexible. They limit their bookings so that they can accommodate for walk-ins.

BERNS ASIATISKA ⑩

ASIAN • FASHIONABLE • ELEGANT

Berns Hotel • Näckströmsgatan 8, Berzelii Park ⊠ 111 47 **PLAN: C2**
Ⓜ Kungsträdgården
TEL. 08-566 327 67 – **www**.berns.se

Menu 795 SEK – Carte 399/735 SEK

Within the Berns hotel is this stunning rococo ballroom with a terrace overlooking Berzelii Park. The extensive Asian fusion menu covers everything from Chinese to Indian and includes bento boxes, sushi, sharing dishes and weekend brunches.

BOBERGS ⭐️🍴

MODERN CUISINE • ELEGANT • CLASSIC DÉCOR

XxX &. [AC]

NK Department Store, Hamngatan 18-20 (4th floor)
✉ 111 47 PLAN: B2
Ⓜ Kungsträdgården
TEL. 08-762 81 61 (booking advisable) – **www**.bobergsmatsal.se
Closed Christmas-New Year, July-mid August and Sunday
Menu 395 SEK – Carte 405/615 SEK (lunch only)

Head past the canteen in this historic department store to the elegant birch-panelled room and ask for a river view. Choose the set business lunch or from the seasonal à la carte; classic cooking mixes French and Swedish influences.

BOQUERIA 🍴

SPANISH • TAPAS BAR • FASHIONABLE

X &. 🏠

Jakobsbergsgatan 17 ✉ 111 44 PLAN: B2
Ⓜ Hötorget
TEL. 08-30 74 00 – **www**.boqueria.se
Closed 24-25 December, 1 January and midsummer
Menu 145 SEK (weekday lunch) – Carte 370/995 SEK

A vibrant, bustling tapas restaurant with high-level seating, located in a smart mall. Appealing menus offer tapas and a range of authentic dishes for two or more to share. Sangria and pintxos can be enjoyed in their nearby bar.

CAROUSEL 🍴

SWEDISH • CLASSIC DÉCOR • HISTORIC

Gustav Adolfs Torg 20 ⊠ 111 53 PLAN: B2
Ⓜ Kungsträdgården
TEL. 08-10 27 57 – www.restaurantcarousel.se
Closed 24-26 December, midsummer and Sunday

Carte 415/760 SEK

Start with a drink under the impressive original ceiling in the bar then sit near the carousel or out on the terrace. The experienced chefs carefully prepare flavoursome dishes which follow the seasons and have classic Swedish roots.

ERIKS BAKFICKA 🍴

SWEDISH • BISTRO

Fredrikshovsgatan 4 ⊠ 115 23 PLAN: D2
TEL. 08-660 15 99 – www.eriks.se
Closed mid July to mid August, Christmas, Easter, Saturday lunch and Sunday

Carte 420/595 SEK

Set in a residential area close to Djurgårdsbron Bridge and a favourite with the locals. The bistro-style interior has wood-panelling and marble-topped tables. Simple, unpretentious cooking features Swedish classics and a 'dish of the day'.

FARANG 🍴

SOUTH EAST ASIAN • MINIMALIST • FASHIONABLE

XX ♿ A/C

Tulegatan 7 ✉ 113 53 PLAN: B1
Ⓜ Rådmansgatan
TEL. 08-673 74 00 – **www**.farang.se
Closed July, midsummer, Christmas, Sunday and Monday
Menu 245/695 SEK – Carte 375/580 SEK

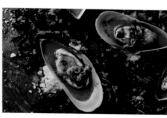

The sister of Farang in Helsinki is this vast restaurant with a chic bar. Cooking focuses on southeast Asia and on hot, sweet and sour tastes; dishes are aromatic, zingy and colourful. Sharing is encouraged and there's a family atmosphere.

GRO 🍴

MODERN CUISINE • SIMPLE • FRIENDLY

X

Sankt Eriksgatan 67 (via Odengatan on Sankt Eriksgatan just before bridge) ✉ 113 32
Ⓜ Sankt Eriksplan
TEL. 08-643 42 22 – **www**.grorestaurang.se
Closed July, 23 December-10 January, Sunday and Monday
Menu 500 SEK (dinner only)

Formerly a butcher's shop, this is now a simple, relaxed little eatery. Cooking is the chef-owners' take on Swedish classics and uses both traditional and modern techniques; local ingredients, particularly vegetables, play a key role.

HILLENBERG ⊀○

MODERN CUISINE • DESIGN • BRASSERIE   XX

Humlegårdsgatan 14 ⊠ 114 34 PLAN: C1
Ⓜ Östermalmstorg
TEL. 08-519 42153 – www.hillenberg.se
Closed Saturday lunch and Sunday
Menu 395/675 SEK – Carte 385/835 SEK

There's a marble bar on each side of this bright, modern restaurant, where the designer's eye for detail is evident. The food reflects the surroundings by being fresh, contemporary, colourful and free from unnecessary frills.

LISA ELMQVIST ⊀○

SEAFOOD • MINIMALIST   Y

Humlesgårdsgatan 1 ⊠ 114 39 PLAN: C1
Ⓜ Östermalmstorg
TEL. 08-553 40410 – www.lisaelmqvist.se
Closed 24 December, midsummer, bank holidays and Sunday
Carte 425/1050 SEK

While the original 19C market hall is being restored, this established family-run restaurant is operating from the temporary marketplace next door. Top quality seafood from the day's catch features in unfussy, satisfying combinations.

LUZETTE ❚○

SWEDISH • BRASSERIE • DESIGN

Centralstationen, Centralplan 25 ✉ 111 20 PLAN: B2
Ⓜ T-Centralen
TEL. 08-519 316 00 – **www**.luzette.se
Carte 425/715 SEK

A modern brasserie and takeaway in the Central train station, inspired
by the grand restaurants of old. Its name means 'light' and refers to
the 1920s luminaire designed by Peter Behrens. Swedish cooking
features rotisserie specials.

NIKLAS ❚○

MODERN CUISINE • FASHIONABLE • BISTRO   XX

Regeringsgatan 66 ✉ 111 39 PLAN: B2
Ⓜ Hötorget
TEL. 08-20 60 10 – **www**.niklas.se
Closed 24-25 December, 1 January, midsummer, Saturday lunch and
Sunday

Carte 330/675 SEK

Contemporary, industrial-style bistro with large blackboard menus
on the walls. The owner's extensive travels guide the menus for the
next 6 months. You can also try the 'Punk Gastronomy' dinner menu
in the adjoining nightclub Weds-Sat.

NOSH AND CHOW ⑩

INTERNATIONAL • BRASSERIE • FASHIONABLE

XX 🕭 AC ⬡

Norrlandsgatan 24 ✉ 111 43 PLAN: B2
Ⓜ Hötorget
TEL. 08-503 389 60 – www.noshandchow.se
Closed 24 December, 1 January, lunch in summer, midsummer, bank holidays and Sunday

Carte 365/790 SEK

This former bank has been transformed into a glitzy cocktail bar and brasserie which displays a smart mix of New York and New England styling. Filling dishes blend French, American and Swedish influences with other global flavours.

POCKET ⑩

TRADITIONAL CUISINE • BISTRO • SIMPLE

X AC ⬡

Brunnsgatan 1 ✉ 111 38 PLAN: B1
Ⓜ Östermalmstorg
TEL. 08-545 273 00 (bookings not accepted) – www.pontusfrithiof.com
Closed July-mid August, Saturday lunch, Monday dinner, Sunday and bank holidays

Menu 995 SEK – Carte 325/415 SEK

Grab a table in the window of this casual bistro or sit at the counter to watch the chefs at work. Menus offer French bistro classics with some Swedish influences; start with a selection of snacks – three are equal to a starter.

SHIBUMI ㍿

JAPANESE • INTIMATE • MINIMALIST

Kungstensgatan 2 ⊠ 114 25 PLAN: B1
Ⓜ Tekniska Högskolan
TEL. 08-696 23 10 (booking advisable) – **www**.shibumi.se
Closed Christmas, Easter, midsummer, Sunday and Monday
Carte 245/405 SEK (dinner only)

This discreet modern restaurant is based on a Japanese izakaya. It's open until late and comes with an underground buzz – and not just because it's in a basement. Expect plenty of original dishes and a daily changing cocktail list.

SMAK ㍿

CREATIVE • TRENDY

Oxtorgsgatan 14 ⊠ 104 35 PLAN: B2
Ⓜ Hötorget
TEL. 08-22 09 52 (booking essential) – **www**.restaurangentm.com
Closed Christmas, Easter, Sunday and lunch Saturday
Menu 400/600 SEK

Smak means 'taste' and at dinner you choose 3, 5 or 7 modern small plates according to their flavour (lunch offers express set menus). The large room features striking brass lamps and the walls are hung with mirrors and tapestries.

SPECERIET ₤○

CLASSIC CUISINE • SIMPLE

Artillerigatan 14 ⊠ 114 51 PLAN: C2
Ⓜ Östermalmstorg
TEL. 08-662 30 60 – **www**.speceriet.se
Closed Christmas-New Year, Sunday, lunch Saturday and Monday
Carte 325/495 SEK

The more casual addendum to the Gastrologik restaurant will get
you in the mood for sharing. Sit at communal tables and choose from
three main dishes at lunchtime and a wider selection of mix and match
dishes at dinner.

STRANDVÄGEN 1 ₤○

INTERNATIONAL • DESIGN • ELEGANT

Strandvägen 1 ⊠ 114 51 PLAN: C2
Ⓜ Kungsträdgården
TEL. 08-663 80 00 – **www**.strandvagen1.se
Closed 24 December
Carte 425/765 SEK

Sit on the terrace of this modern bistro-style restaurant – a former
bank – and watch the boats bobbing up and down in the harbour.
Seasonal menus offer generously proportioned, globally inspired
dishes with bold flavours.

STUREHOF ⅋♨

SEAFOOD • BRASSERIE •
FASHIONABLE

Stureplan 2 ✉ 114 46 PLAN: C1
Ⓜ Östermalmstorg
TEL. 08-40 57 30 – www.sturehof.com
Carte 445/895 SEK

This bustling city institution dates back over a century and is a
wonderful mix of the traditional and the modern. It boasts a buzzing
terrace, several marble-topped bars and a superb food court. Classic
menus specialise in seafood.

SVARTENGRENS ⅋♨

MEATS AND GRILLS • FRIENDLY • NEIGHBOURHOOD

Tulegatan 24 ✉ 113 53 PLAN: B1
Ⓜ Tekniska Högskolan
TEL. 08-612 65 50 (booking advisable) – www.svartengrens.se
Closed Christmas and midsummer
Menu 725 SEK – Carte 315/845 SEK (dinner only)

The eponymous chef-owner has created a modern bistro specialising
in sustainable meat and veg from producers in the archipelago. Along
with smoking and pickling, the dry-ageing is done in-house, and the
cuts change daily.

VASSA EGGEN ⁂

MEATS AND GRILLS • FASHIONABLE • RUSTIC ⠀⠀⠀⠀XX AC

Elite H. Stockholm Plaza • Birger Jarlsgatan 29 ✉ 103 95 PLAN: B1
Ⓜ Östermalmstorg
TEL. 08-216169 – **www**.vassaeggen.com
Closed midsummer, Christmas, Saturday lunch and Sunday
Menu 695 SEK – Carte 495/1000 SEK

A pleasant bar leads through to a dimly lit hotel dining room where bold artwork hangs on the walls. Hearty Swedish cooking relies on age-old recipes, with a particular focus on meat; whole beasts are butchered and hung on-site.

WEDHOLMS FISK ⁂

SEAFOOD • INTIMATE • ELEGANT ⠀⠀⠀⠀XX AC ⟠

Nybrokajen 17 ✉ 111 48 PLAN: C2
Ⓜ Kungsträdgården
TEL. 08-611 78 74 (booking essential) – **www**.wedholmsfisk.se
Closed 23 December-7 January, midsummer, bank holidays, lunch 26 June-14 August, Saturday lunch and Sunday
Carte 530/1195 SEK

An impressive former auction house set beside the financial institutions on Stockholm's 'Little Wall Street', overlooking the harbour. It's owned by a large fishmonger's which has its own boats; in winter, go for their speciality – turbot.

ZINK GRILL ⅋○

FRENCH · BISTRO · TRADITIONAL DÉCOR

Biblioteksgatan 5 ✉ 111 46 **PLAN: C2**
🚇 Östermalmstorg
TEL. 08-611 42 22 – **www**.zinkgrill.se
Closed Christmas and midsummer
Carte 327/633 SEK

This lively, late night bistro is one of Stockholm's oldest restaurants and the purchase of its French zinc bar – dating from 1933 – is how it all began. The Gallic and Italian inspired menu features plenty of charcuterie and grills.

GRAND

LUXURY · HISTORIC BUILDING · ELEGANT

Södra Blasieholmshamnen 6 ✉ 103 27 **PLAN: C2**
🚇 Kungsträdgården
TEL. 08-679 35 00 – **www**.mdghs.com
278 rm ☕ – 🛏 3600/4200 SEK 🛏🛏 4900/5800 SEK – 34 suites
MATHIAS DAHLGREN-MATBAREN ❀ – See restaurant listing

The Grand certainly lives up to its name with its Corinthian columns, handsome panelled bar and impressive spa. Classical bedrooms have marble-decked bathrooms and those at the front have great views over the water to the Old Town. Dining choices include Verandan, with its harbour outlook and smörgåsbords, lively Matbaren and another new restaurant from Mathias Dahlgren which is set to open in 2017.

NOBIS

HISTORIC • DESIGN • PERSONALISED

Norrmalmstorg 2-4 ⊠ 111 86 **PLAN: C2**
Ⓜ Östermalmstorg
TEL. 08-614 10 00 – **www**.nobishotel.com
201 rm – ♦ 1890/2290 SEK ♦♦ 2290/2690 SEK, ⊊ 175 SEK – 1 suite

It started life as two Royal Palaces and later became a bank (the famous 'Stockholm Syndrome' robbery took place here); now it's a smart hotel with two internal courtyards and spacious bedrooms with clean lines, African wood furnishings and marble bathrooms. Dine on refined Italian dishes in Caina or more rustic, wholesome ones in Bakfica, with its pavement terrace.

SHERATON

BUSINESS • CHAIN • MODERN

Tegelbacken 6 ⊠ 101 23 **PLAN: B2**
Ⓜ T-Centralen
TEL. 08-412 36 02 – **www**.sheratonstockholm.com
465 rm – ♦ 1395/5185 SEK ♦♦ 1395/5185 SEK, ⊊ 259 SEK – 29 suites

This was the first Sheraton to open in Europe, back in 1971, and its unassuming concrete façade is now a listed feature. Bedrooms are smart, spacious and understated, and some overlook Lake Mälaren or the Old Town. The lively restaurant offers international buffet lunches and traditional Swedish dinners.

BERNS

HISTORIC BUILDING · BOUTIQUE HOTEL · DESIGN
♨ ⅃⅃ 🦽

Näckströmsgatan 8, Berzelii Park ✉ 111 47 PLAN: C2
Ⓜ Kungsträdgården
TEL. 08-566 322 00 – www.berns.se
82 rm – ♦ 1100/3300 SEK ♦♦ 1200/3500 SEK, ☕ 195 SEK – 6 suites
BERNS ASIATISKA – See restaurant listing

In 1863 Heinrich Robert Berns opened Stockholm's biggest concert and party hall on this site and, continuing that tradition, events are a big part of this hotel's business. Bedrooms are modern; some have seating areas or balconies.

DIPLOMAT

TRADITIONAL · LUXURY · ELEGANT
≼ ♨ ♒ ⅃⅃ 🦽

Strandvägen 7c ✉ 114 56 PLAN: C2
Ⓜ Kungsträdgården
TEL. 08-459 68 00 – www.diplomathotel.com
129 rm – ♦ 1750/3950 SEK ♦♦ 2250/4450 SEK, ☕ 275 SEK – 3 suites

Early 20C charm combines with modern furnishings in this art nouveau hotel. Take the old cage lift up to the cosy library, which leads through to a sweet little cocktail bar. Elegant bedrooms come in pastel hues and some have harbour views. T Bar (the old tea salon) serves Scandinavian-inspired brasserie dishes.

CENTRE

ELITE EDEN PARK

BUSINESS • CONTEMPORARY • MODERN

Sturegatan 22 ✉ 114 36 PLAN: C1
Ⓜ Östermalmstorg
TEL. 08-555 627 00 – **www**.elite.se
124 rm ☲ – 🛉 1300/2850 SEK 🛉🛉 1500/3500 SEK – 1 suite

Smart hotel in a converted office block, designed with the business traveller in mind. Stylish bedrooms boast comfy beds and large showers – some rooms overlook the park and some have small balconies. Choose from an Asian-inspired menu in Miss Voon or traditional British pub dishes in The Bishops Arms.

GRAND CENTRAL BY SCANDIC

BUSINESS • CHAIN • CONTEMPORARY

Kungsgatan 70 ✉ 111 20 PLAN: B2
Ⓜ T-Centralen
TEL. 08-512 520 00 – **www**.scandichotels.com/grandcentral
391 rm ☲ – 🛉 1050/3200 SEK 🛉🛉 1150/3700 SEK – 4 suites

The décor of this contemporary hotel ties in with the arts theme of the area and its old Victorian theatre hosts live music and events. Bedrooms range from 'Cozy' (in the windowless basement) to spacious, well-equipped suites. The coffee shop serves snacks and the restaurant Swedish classics.

HAYMARKET BY SCANDIC

BUSINESS • HISTORIC BUILDING • ART DÉCO

Hötorget 13-15 ✉ 111 57 PLAN: B2
Ⓜ Hötorget
TEL. 08-517 267 00 – www.scandichotels.com
405 rm ♥ – ♦ 1050/3200 SEK ♦♦ 1150/3700 SEK – 16 suites

Built in the 1900s, this former department store sits overlooking the Square, just across from the Concert Hall. Swedish-born Greta Garbot once worked here and the decor, particularly in the bedrooms, gives a nod to the art deco style. There's a small movie theatre, a healthy café-cum-bistro, a European restaurant and an American bar which hosts jazz at weekends.

MISS CLARA BY NOBIS

BUSINESS • MODERN • PERSONALISED

Sveavägen 48 ✉ 111 34 PLAN: B1
Ⓜ Hötorget
TEL. 08-440 67 00 – www.missclarahotel.com
90 rm – ♦ 1590/2790 SEK ♦♦ 1690/3190 SEK, ♥ 169 SEK – 2 suites

A fashionable hotel in a great location; it used to be a girls' school and its name is that of the former principal. Surprisingly quiet, dark wood bedrooms have good facilities. The atmospheric brasserie offers an international menu with an Italian slant and some classic Swedish specialities.

RADISSON BLU STRAND

BUSINESS • HISTORIC BUILDING • CONTEMPORARY

Nybrokajen 9 box 16396 ⊠ 103 27 PLAN: C2
Ⓜ Kungsträdgården
TEL. 08-50 6 640 00 –
www.radissonblu.com/strandhotel-stockholm
160 rm – ♦ 1295/2695 SEK ♦♦ 1395/2995 SEK, ☕ 170 SEK – 11 suites

This imposing hotel part-dates from the 1912 Olympics and sits in a lively waterside spot overlooking Nybroviken. Bedrooms are a mix of traditional and modern styles; the Tower Suite boasts a roof terrace with stunning city views. Enjoy a mix of local and global dishes in the airy atrium restaurant.

ETT HEM

LUXURY • DESIGN • CLASSIC

Sköldungagatan 2 ⊠ 114 27 PLAN: B1
Ⓜ Tekniska Högskolan
TEL. 08-20 05 90 – www.etthem.se
12 rm ☕ – ♦ 3900 SEK ♦♦ 3900/7900 SEK

A charming Arts and Crafts townhouse built as a private residence in 1910. It's elegant, understated and makes good use of wood; its name means 'home' and that's exactly how it feels. Bedroom No.6 features an old chimney and No.1 has a four-poster and a huge marble bath. Modern set menus use top seasonal produce and are served in the kitchen, library or orangery.

LYDMAR

TOWNHOUSE • PERSONALISED • DESIGN

Södra Blasieholmshamnen 2 ✉ 111 48 PLAN: C2
Ⓜ Kungsträdgården
TEL. 08-22 31 60 – www.lydmar.com
46 rm ⌷ – 👤 2700/3800 SEK 👥 3100/5200 SEK – 6 suites

Superbly located across the water from the Palace, is this charming townhouse; formerly the store for the neighbouring museum's archives. It has a relaxed yet funky vibe and regularly changing contemporary artwork – and the roof terrace with its water feature is a delightful spot come summer. The attractive restaurant offers a modern European brasserie menu.

ELITE H. STOCKHOLM PLAZA

BUSINESS • CHAIN • CONTEMPORARY

Birger Jarlsgatan 29 ✉ 103 95 PLAN: B1
Ⓜ Östermalmstorg
TEL. 08-566 220 00 – www.elite.se
143 rm ⌷ – 👤 1290/2890 SEK 👥 1690/3290 SEK – 12 suites
VASSA EGGEN – See restaurant listing

The smaller sister of the Elite Eden Park is this attractive, centrally located building with a façade dating from 1884. Bright fabrics stand out against neutral walls in the compact modern bedrooms; go for one of the corner suites.

KUNGSTRÄDGÅRDEN

TOWNHOUSE • HISTORIC • PERSONALISED

⚔ ⛷ 🧖 AC

Västra Trädgårdsgatan 11b ⊠ 10216 **PLAN: B2**
Ⓜ Kungsträdgården
TEL. 08-440 66 50 – **www**.hotelkungstradgarden.se
98 rm ⌖ – 🛉 1090/2890 SEK 🛉🛉 1350/3250 SEK

Overlooking the park of the same name is this part-18C building with a classical façade and attractive original features. Bedrooms are individually furnished in a Gustavian-style – it's worth paying the extra for a bigger room. A concise menu of French-inspired dishes is served in the covered courtyard.

RIDDARGATAN

BUSINESS • MODERN • PERSONALISED

🛎

Riddargatan 14 ⊠ 114 35 **PLAN: C2**
Ⓜ Östermalmstorg
TEL. 08-555 730 00 – **www**.profilhotels.com
78 rm ⌖ – 🛉 1200/2000 SEK 🛉🛉 1400/2450 SEK – 4 suites

This smart former office block is situated close to the shops and restaurants, and feels very much like a home-from-home. The newer bedrooms have bright, bold designs and modern wet rooms (some of the older rooms are currently being refurbished). The contemporary breakfast room doubles as a lively bar.

TIME

BUSINESS • MODERN • PERSONALISED

♿ 🦢 🛁 🚗

Vanadisvägen 12 ✉ 113 46 **PLAN: A1**
Ⓜ Odenplan
TEL. 08-545 473 00 – **www**.timehotel.se
144 rm ☕ – 👤 1850/2120 SEK 👥 2050/2250 SEK

This purpose-built business hotel sits in a smart residential area on the edge of town and is run by a friendly, hands-on team. Bedrooms are bright, airy and of a good size; Superiors have Juliet balconies and Studios offer long-term lets.

CLARION COLLECTION
H. WELLINGTON

BUSINESS • TOWNHOUSE • TRADITIONAL

♿ 🦢 🚗

Storgatan 6 ✉ 114 51 **PLAN: C1**
Ⓜ Östermalmstorg
TEL. 08-667 09 10 – **www**.wellington.se
Closed 22 December-4 January
61 rm ☕ – 👤 820/2420 SEK 👥 1420/3220 SEK – 1 suite

Set in a former office block, this centrally located hotel makes an ideal base for shopping and sightseeing. Simple bedrooms feature bright fabrics and those on the top floor have city views. Buffet dinners are included in the price.

DEN GYLDENE FREDEN

TRADITIONAL CUISINE • RUSTIC • INN

Österlånggatan 51 ⊠ 10 317 PLAN: F1
Ⓜ Gamla Stan
TEL. 08-24 97 60 (booking essential) – www.gyldenefreden.se
Closed Sunday
Menu 265/470 SEK – Carte 405/775 SEK

Built by a vintner in 1722, this historic property is thought to be the city's oldest restaurant. It was bequeathed to the Swedish Academy in 1920 and they continue to meet here weekly. Both the ground floor and the cellar are hugely characterful. Cooking sees refined, modern versions of Swedish classics.

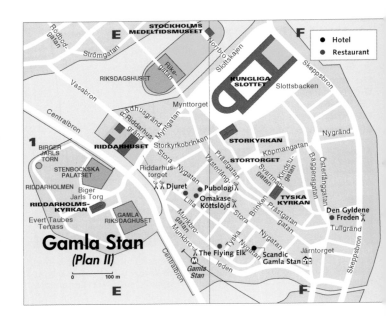

DJURET 🍴

MEATS AND GRILLS • RUSTIC • NEIGHBOURHOOD ✕✕ 🦀

Lilla Nygatan 5 ✉ 111 28 **PLAN: E1**
Ⓜ Gamla Stan
TEL. 08-506 40 084 (booking essential) – **www**.djuret.se
Closed Christmas, July and Sunday
Menu 595 SEK (dinner only)

It's all about meat here at Djuret. A different beast features on the
menu every two weeks – maybe wild boar or reindeer – and there's
an excellent selection of wines to accompany. Dine in the 'Meat' room
or the 'Trophy' room.

THE FLYING ELK 🍴

MODERN CUISINE • INN • FRIENDLY ✕

Mälartorget 15 ✉ 111 27 **PLAN: F1**
Ⓜ Gamla Stan
TEL. 08-20 85 83 – **www**.theflyingelk.se
Closed 24-25, 31 December, 1 January and midsummer
Menu 695 SEK – Carte 315/710 SEK (dinner only and lunch Saturday
and Sunday)

A good night out is guaranteed at this lively corner spot, which is
modelled on a British pub and has several different bars. Choose
from bar snacks, pub dishes with a twist or a popular tasting menu of
refined modern classics.

OMAKASE KÖTTSLÖJD ⑩

SWEDISH • COSY • TRENDY

Yxsmedsgränd 12 ⊠ 111 28 **PLAN: E1**
Ⓜ Gamla Stan
TEL. 08-506 400 80 (booking essential) –
www.omakasekottslojd.se
Closed Christmas-New Year, July and Sunday-Tuesday
Menu 1195 SEK (dinner only) (tasting menu only)

There's plenty of interaction between the chefs and diners at this small restaurant which seats just 16. The chefs pick up to 20 dishes to serve and cooking is an unusual cross between Japanese sushi and home-cured Swedish charcuterie.

PUBOLOGI ⑩

CREATIVE • FRIENDLY • RUSTIC

Stora Nygatan 20 ⊠ 111 27 **PLAN: E1**
Ⓜ Gamla Stan
TEL. 08-506 400 86 (booking advisable) – **www**.pubologi.se
Closed Christmas-New Year, July and Sunday
Menu 695 SEK (dinner only)

A modern, wine-orientated bistro, with one long communal table and several smaller ones; the menus and cutlery are in illuminated drawers in the table. Cooking is fairly elaborate and good use is made of the chargrill.

SCANDIC GAMLA STAN

TOWNHOUSE • HISTORIC • COSY

Lilla Nygatan 25 ⊠ 111 28 PLAN: F1
Ⓜ Gamla Stan
TEL. 08-517 383 00 – **www**.scandichotels.se
52 rm ⬚ – ♦ 845/1908 SEK ♦♦ 1424/2108 SEK

A historic townhouse dating from the 17C, located on a cobbled street in the heart of the Old Town. Bedrooms are cosy and decorated in a traditional Swedish style; bathrooms are modern. The roof terrace offers great city views.

OAXEN KROG ✿✿

CREATIVE • DESIGN • FRIENDLY

Beckholmsvägen 26 (off Djurgårdsvägen) ⊠ 115 21 PLAN: D3
TEL. 08-55 153 105 (booking essential) – **www**.oaxen.com
Closed 21 December-13 January, Easter, midsummer, Sunday-Monday and Tuesday January-March
Menu 1800/2100 SEK (dinner only)

Chef:
Magnus Ek
Specialities:
Turbot with pickled elderflower sauce. Glazed pork with garlic, woodruff and spring onion. Sweet cicely sorbet with milk foam and rhubarb.

This rebuilt boat shed sits in a delightful waterside location. Diners are led through a secret door in Oaxen Slip into an oak-furnished room with a natural, slightly nautical feel. Choose 6 or 10 courses of 'New Nordic' cuisine: beautifully constructed dishes are allied to nature and the seasons – they're delicate and balanced but also offer real depth of flavour.

OAXEN SLIP 😊

TRADITIONAL CUISINE · BISTRO

Beckholmsvägen 26 (off Djurgårdsvägen) ✉ 115 21 **PLAN: D3**
TEL. 08-55153105 – www.oaxen.com
Closed Christmas and New Year
Carte 265/620 SEK

A bright, bustling bistro next to the old slipway; try for a spot on the delightful terrace. Light floods the room and boats hang from the girders in a nod to the local shipbuilding industry. The food is wholesome and heartening and features plenty of seafood – whole fish dishes are a speciality.

ULLA WINBLADH 😊

SWEDISH · CLASSIC DÉCOR · COSY

Rosendalsvägen 8 ✉ 115 21 **PLAN: D2**
TEL. 08-534 897 01 (booking essential) – **www**.ullawinbladh.se
Closed 24-25 December
Menu 515 SEK – Carte 260/625 SEK

Ulla Winbladh was originally built as a steam bakery for the 1897 Stockholm World Fair and is set in charming parkland beside the Skansen open-air museum. Sit on the terrace or in the older, more characterful part of the building. Hearty Swedish dishes include sweet and sour herring and fish roe.

POP HOUSE

BOUTIQUE HOTEL • PERSONALISED • MINIMALIST

欿 ﾖ ぬ AC

Djurgårdsvägen 68 ⊠ 115 21 PLAN: D2
TEL. 08-502 54 140 – www.pophouse.se
49 rm ⌤ – ♦ 1195/3095 SEK ♦♦ 1295/3295 SEK – 2 suites

Pop House is ideally placed for visitors to the parks and museums of Djurgården. Bypass the queues waiting to enter 'ABBA The Museum', and head up to one of the spacious, simply furnished bedrooms; most have balconies with pleasant views. The small lounge, bar and restaurant are open-plan.

SKEPPSHOLMEN

HISTORIC • DESIGN • PERSONALISED

≼ ⅏ ⌂ 欿 ﾖ ✖ ぬ AC 𝄃 P

Gröna Gången 1 ⊠ 111 99 PLAN: D2
TEL. 08-407 23 00 – www.hotelskeppsholmen.se
81 rm ⌤ – ♦ 1495/2995 SEK ♦♦ 1495/2995 SEK – 1 suite

This 17C hotel is perfect for a peaceful stay close to the city. It's set on a small island beside a beautiful park and was built by the king in 1699 for his soldiers (the conference room was once the officers' mess). White bedrooms have a minimalist style and sea or park views. Menus feature Swedish recipes.

NOOK 😋

MODERN CUISINE • INTIMATE • FRIENDLY   ⚔

Åsögatan 176 (South: 3 km by C3) ✉ 116 32 PLAN: D3
Ⓜ Medborgarplatsen
TEL. 08-702 12 22 (booking advisable) – **www**.nookrestaurang.se
Closed Christmas, July, Sunday and Monday
Menu 380 SEK – Carte 380/430 SEK (dinner only)

This modern restaurant offers great value. Drop into the bar for Asian-influenced snacks or head to the intimately lit dining room with its checkerboard floor for one of two set menus. Creative cooking blends Swedish ingredients with Korean influences; order 3 days ahead for the suckling pig feast.

HÄKTET 🍴

MODERN CUISINE • BISTRO • SIMPLE   ⚔ 🏠 ✧

Hornsgatan 82 (South: 3 km by C3) ✉ 118 21 PLAN: B3
Ⓜ Zinkensdamn
TEL. 08-84 59 10 – **www**.haktet.se
Closed 24 and 31 December, 1 January, midsummer and Sunday
Carte 360/540 SEK (dinner only)

From 1781-1872 this was a debtors' prison. It has a characterful courtyard terrace and three bars – one in the style of a speakeasy, with a secret door. The simple bistro at the back serves classic Swedish recipes with a modern edge.

WOODSTOCKHOLM ⭐🍴

MODERN CUISINE • BISTRO • NEIGHBOURHOOD 🍴 ⛱ ⟠

Mosebacke Torg 9 ✉ 116 46 PLAN: C3
Ⓜ Slussen
TEL. 08-36 93 99 – www.woodstockholm.com
Closed Christmas-New Year, midsummer, Sunday and Monday
Menu 575 SEK – Carte 455/575 SEK (dinner only)

A chef-turned-furniture-maker owns this neighbourhood restaurant overlooking the park. Cooking follows a theme which changes every 2 months and dishes are simple yet full of flavour. In summer, the private room opens as a wine bar.

RIVAL

BOUTIQUE HOTEL • BUSINESS • PERSONALISED
⛲ ♿ 🛎

Mariatorget 3 (South: 3 km by C3) ✉ 118 91 PLAN: B3
Ⓜ Mariatorget
TEL. 08-545 789 00 – www.rival.se
99 rm – 🛏 1395/4995 SEK 🛏🛏 1395/4995 SEK, ⟐ 175 SEK – 2 suites

The location is delightful: opposite a beautiful square with gardens and a fountain. It's owned by ABBA's Benny Andersson and the stylish bedrooms come with Swedish movie themes and murals of famous scenes; the 700-seater art deco theatre also hosts regular events and shows. Dine on global dishes either in the bistro or on the balcony; the café is popular for snacks.

CLARION H. ARLANDA AIRPORT

BUSINESS • MODERN • FUNCTIONAL

Tornvägen 2, Sky City (at Terminals 4-5, 1st floor above street level) ✉ 190 45
TEL. 08-444 18 00 - **www**.choice.se/clarion/arlandaairport.se
414 rm ☕ - 🚹 990/2890 SEK 🚹🚹 1190/3090 SEK - 13 suites

A sleek, corporate hotel next to Terminals 4 and 5, with sound eco-credentials - they even make honey from their own hives. Relax in the large 'living room' style lounge area or in the outside pool, then have dinner in the bistro which offers a mix of international and Swedish dishes along with runway views.

RADISSON BLU SKY CITY

BUSINESS • MODERN • FUNCTIONAL

Sky City (at Terminals 4-5, 2nd floor above street level) ✉ 190 45
TEL. 08-506 740 00 -
www.radissonblu.com/skycityhotel-arlanda
260 rm - 🚹 1595/2895 SEK 🚹🚹 1595/2895 SEK, ☕ 150 SEK - 1 suite

This comfy business hotel enjoys a unique location, looking out over the atrium of the airport terminal as well as the runway. Well-soundproofed bedrooms come in three different styles; go for 'Business Class' for more space and amenities. The restaurant serves a blend of Swedish classics and more global dishes.

STALLMÄSTAREGÅRDEN

INN • HISTORIC BUILDING • HISTORIC

🛏 🍴 ⚲ 🅿

Nortull (North: 2 km by Sveavägen) ✉ 113 47
TEL. 08-610 13 00 – www.stallmastaregarden.se
Closed 24-30 December
49 rm ☕ – 🛉 1495/2995 SEK 🛉🛉 1495/2995 SEK – 3 suites

You can enjoy beautiful views over the water to the Royal Park from
this brightly painted inn, which dates from the 17C. It comprises
several buildings set around a garden courtyard. Cosy bedrooms
have a classic style and Oriental touches. Modern Swedish cuisine is
influenced by classic Tore Wretman recipes.

VILLA KÄLLHAGEN

TRADITIONAL • BUSINESS • MINIMALIST

⟨ 🛥 🛏 🍴 🌀 Ⓐⓒ ⚲ 🅿

Djurgårdsbrunnsvägen 10 (East: 3 km by Strandvägen) ✉ 115 27
TEL. 08-665 03 00 – www.kallhagen.se
36 rm ☕ – 🛉 1295/2795 SEK 🛉🛉 1495/2995 SEK – 3 suites

This well-run hotel is a popular place for functions, but with its idyllic
waterside location, it's a hit with leisure guests too. Bedrooms feature
four different colour schemes – inspired by the seasons – and have
park or water views. The modern Swedish menu has a classic edge
and comes with wine pairings.

FJÄDERHOLMARNAS KROG ⅋○

SEAFOOD • FRIENDLY • RUSTIC

Stora Fjäderholmen (East: 25 minutes by boat from Södermalm, or 5 minutes from Nacka Strand) ✉ 111 15
TEL. 08-718 833 55 (booking essential) –
www.fjaderholmarnaskrog.se
Closed 17-28 April, 29 September-22 November and 22 December-31 March
Menu 395/495 SEK – Carte 405/880 SEK

The location is idyllic and on a sunny day nothing beats a spot on the terrace watching the ships glide through the archipelago. The airy interior has a boathouse feel. Classic seafood dishes are replaced by a buffet table at Christmas.

RESTAURANT J ⅋○

SWEDISH • BRASSERIE

Hotel J • Ellensviksvägen 1 (Southeast: 10 km by Stadsgården) ✉ 131 28
TEL. 08-601 30 25 – **www**.hotelj.com
Closed 25-30 December and 1-10 January
Carte dinner 360/705 SEK

A short stroll along the waterfront from Hotel J is its long, narrow restaurant. Huge windows and a lovely terrace make the most of the marina setting (it's just 20min from the city by boat). Swedish dishes mix with global fare.

HOTEL J

HISTORIC • DESIGN

⇐ 🛥 🪑 ⚔ ♿ AC ⛷ P

Ellensviksvägen 1 (Southeast: 10 km by Stadsgården) ✉ 131 28
TEL. 08-6013000 – **www**.hotelj.com

158 rm ☲ – ♦ 1290/2990 SEK ♦♦ 1290/2990 SEK – 4 suites

RESTAURANT J – See restaurant listing

This was once the summer house of a local politician and a relaxed
atmosphere still pervades. Maritime knick-knacks feature in the
charming guest areas and bedrooms have a quirky New England style;
many overlook the water.

LUX DAG FÖR DAG ⭑○

MODERN CUISINE • BRASSERIE •
NEIGHBOURHOOD   XX ⇐ ♿ 🏠 AC

Primusgatan 116 (West: 5.5 km by Norr Mälarstrand) ✉ 112 67
TEL. 08-6190190 – **www**.luxdagfordag.se
Closed 23 December-2 January, 16 July-16 August and Sunday-
Monday

Carte 345/655 SEK

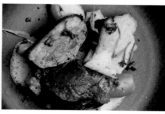

A bright, modern, brasserie-style restaurant in an old waterside
Electrolux factory dating back to 1916. Generously proportioned
dishes might look modern but they have a traditional base; sourcing
ingredients locally is paramount.

BOCKHOLMEN 🍴

SWEDISH • TRADITIONAL DÉCOR •
COUNTRY HOUSE XX ⪝ 🏠 ⇕ **P**

Bockholmsvägen (Northwest: 7 km by Sveavägen and E18) ✉ 170 78
Ⓜ Bergshamra
TEL. 08-624 22 00 (booking essential) – **www**.bockholmen.com
Closed 20 December-6 January, midsummer and
lunch October-April

Carte 290/665 SEK

With charming terraces leading down to the water and an outside bar,
this 19C summer house is the perfect place to relax on a summer's day.
It's set on a tiny island, so opening times vary. Wide-ranging menus
include weekend brunch.

ULRIKSDALS WÄRDSHUS 🍴

TRADITIONAL CUISINE • INN XX ⪝   ⇕ **P**

Ulriksdals Slottspark (Northwest: 8 km by Sveavägen and E 18
towards Norrtälje then take first junction for Ulriksdals Slott)
✉ 170 79
Ⓜ Bergshamra
TEL. 08-85 08 15 (booking essential) – **www**.ulriksdalswardshus.se
Closed Monday dinner

Menu 285 SEK (weekday lunch)/485 SEK – Carte 450/745 SEK

A charming 19C wooden inn located in the park, with traditional winter
garden styling and a lovely wine cellar. Classic Swedish dishes are
supplemented by a smörgåsbord at lunch. Start with drinks on the
terrace overlooking the lake.

GOTHENBURG

Sweden

D. Schoenen/imageBROKER/age fotostock

Gothenburg is considered to be one of Sweden's friendliest towns, a throwback to its days as a leading trading centre. This is a compact, pretty city whose roots go back four hundred years. It has trams, broad avenues and canals and its centre is boisterous but never feels tourist heavy or overcrowded. Gothenburgers take life at a more leisurely pace than their Stockholm cousins over on the east coast. The mighty shipyards that once dominated the shoreline are now quiet; go to the centre, though, and you find the good-time

ambience of Avenyn, a vivacious thoroughfare full of places in which to shop, eat and drink. But for those still itching for a feel of the heavy industry that once defined the place, there's a Volvo museum sparkling with chrome and shiny steel. The Old Town is the historic heart of the city: its tight grid of streets has grand façades and a fascinating waterfront. Just west is the Vasastan quarter, full of fine National Romantic buildings. Further west again is Haga, an old working-class district which has been gentrified, its cobbled streets sprawling with trendy cafes and boutiques. Adjacent to Haga is the district of Linné, a vibrant area with its elegantly tall 19th century Dutch-inspired buildings. As this is a maritime town, down along the quayside is as good a place to get your bearings as any.

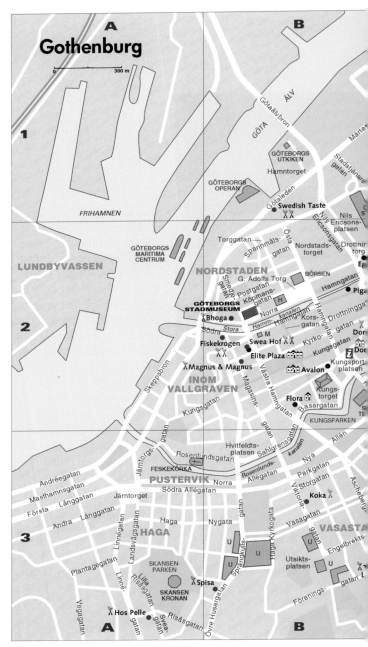

Gothenburg

0 ——— 300 m

GÖTA ÄLV
GÖTA
Götaälvbron

GÖTEBORGS UTKIKEN
Hamntorget

GÖTEBORGS OPERAN
Götaleden

Swedish Taste

FRIHAMNEN

Nils Ericsonsplatsen

Torggatan
S.Spannmålsgatan   Östra Nordstadstorget
GÖTEBORGS MARITIMA CENTRUM

Drottningtorg

NORDSTADEN
G. Adolfs Torg   BÖRSEN
Smedjegatan   Postgatan   Hamngatan
GÖTEBORGS STADMUSEUM   Köpmansgatan   Piga
Norra   H
Bhoga   Hamm-kanalen   Korsgatan
Södra   Stora   Hamngatan   Drottning
Fiskekrogen   M   Swea Hof   Kyrkogatan
Magnus & Magnus   Elite Plaza   Kungsgatan   Dor
INOM VALLGRAVEN   Avalon   Kungsportplatsen
Skeppsbron   Västra Hamngatan   Flora   Kungstorget   TE
Kungsgatan   Magasinsgatan   Basargatan
KUNGSPARKEN

Hvitfeldtsplatsen   Allén
Rosenlundsgatan   Sahlgrensgatan   kanalen   Nya
FESKEKÔRKA   Järntorgsgatan   Rosenlunds-   Parkgatan   Aschebergs
PUSTERVIK   Norra   Allégatan   Storgatan
Andréegatan   Södra Allégatan   Viktoria   Koka
Masthamnsgatan   Järntorget   Vasagatan   VASASTA
Förstat   Långgatan   Haga   Nygata   Engelbrekts-
Andra   Långgatan   HAGA   Haga Kyrkogata   gatan
Linnégatan   Landsvägsgatan   Sprängkullsgatan   U
Plantagegatan   SKANSENPARKEN   U   Utsiktsplatsen   L
Linné   Lilla Risåsgatan   SKANSEN KRONAN   Spisa   Övre Husargatan   Förenings-
Vegagatan   Sveagatan   Hos Pelle   Risåsgatan

LUNDBYVASSEN

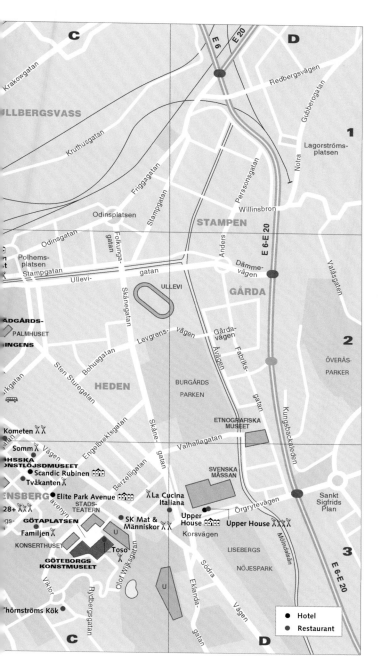

C

E 6
E 20

D

Krakowgatan

ILLBERGSVASS

Kruthusgatan

Redbergsvägen

Gubberogatan

1

Lagorströms-
platsen

Frigagatan

Stampgatan

Notra

Odinsplatsen

Willinsbron

STAMPEN

Perssonsgatan

E 6-E 20

Odinsgatan

Folkunga-
gatan

Anders

Polhems-
platsen

Dämme-
vägen

Valåsgatan

Stampgatan

Ullevi-

gatan

ULLEVI

GÅRDA

ÄDGÅRDS-

PALMHUSET

Skånegatan

Levgrens-

vägen

Gårda-
vägen

2

INGENS

Bohusgatan

Sten Sturegatan

Åvägen

Fabriks-

ÖVERÅS-
PARKER

rkgatan

HEDEN

BURGÅRDS

PARKEN

gatan

Kungsbackaleden

Kometen X X

Engelbrektsgatan

Skåne-

ETNOGRAFISKA
MUSEET

Somm X Vägen

Valhallagatan

gatan

HSSKA
NSTLÖJDSMUSEET

Berzeliigatan

● Scandic Rubinen 🏨

● Tvåkanten X

SVENSKA
MÄSSAN

Sankt
Sigfrids
Plan

NSBERG ● Elite Park Avenue 🏨

X La Cucina
Italiana

avenyn

STADS-
TEATERN

Upper
House 🏨

Örgrytevägen

Upper House X X X

28+ X X X

gs-

GÖTAPLATSEN

● SK Mat &
Människor X X

Korsvägen

● Familjen X

KONSERTHUSET

Toso

LISEBERGS

Mölndalsån

E 6-E 20

3

GÖTEBORGS
KONSTMUSEET

Olof Wijksgatan

NÖJESPARK

hörnströms Kök ●

Viktor

Rydbergsgatan

U

Eklanda-

Södra

Vägen

gatan

U

● Hotel
● Restaurant

C

D

BHOGA ✿

CREATIVE • FRIENDLY • SIMPLE

Norra Hamngatan 10 ⊠ 411 17 PLAN: B2
TEL. 031-13 80 18 – **www**.bhoga.se
Closed 20 December-10 January, 1-7 August, Sunday and Monday
Menu 600/900 SEK (dinner only)

Chef:
Gustav Knutsson and Niclas Yngvesson
Specialities:
New potatoes with raspberries, walnuts and marigolds. Roast duck with fermented garlic. Meadowsweet ice cream with blackcurrant and buckwheat.

A chic, contemporary restaurant with an elegant feel, passionately run by two well-travelled chefs and their charmingly attentive team. Top quality seasonal ingredients are used in innovative and imaginative ways, creating provocative yet harmonious texture and flavour combinations. Wine pairings are original.

KOKA ✿

MODERN CUISINE • DESIGN • NEIGHBOURHOOD

Viktoriagatan 12 ⊠ 411 25 PLAN: B3
TEL. 031-701 79 79 – **www**.restaurangkoka.se
Closed July Sunday-Tuesday, Christmas and Sunday
Menu 480/880 SEK (dinner only) (tasting menu only)

Specialities:
Mackerel with gooseberries and cress. Pork shoulder, marigold and trout roe. Sorrel, seaweed and raspberry.

An understatedly elegant room with wooden planks on the floors and walls and wooden furniture to match. Choose 3, 5 or 7 courses from the daily set menu; dishes are light and refreshingly playful in their approach and fish features highly. Well-chosen wines and smooth service complete the picture.

SJÖMAGASINET ✿

SWEDISH • RUSTIC • COSY

Adolf Edelsvärds gata 5, Klippans Kulturreservat 5 (Southwest:
3.5 km by Andréeg taking Kiel-Klippan exit (Stena Line), or boat
from Rosenlund. Also evenings and weekends in summer from Lilla
Bommens Hamn) ✉ 414 51
TEL. 031-775 59 20 (booking essential) – **www**.sjomagasinet.se
Closed 24 December-5 January, Saturday lunch and Sunday
Menu 625 SEK (lunch)/945 SEK – Carte 675/1225 SEK

Chef:
Gustav Trägårdh

Specialities:
Lobster salad. Steamed turbot with
oyster sauce, truffle and potato
variations. Dark chocolate brioche,
chocolate and peanut crème,
sesame ice-cream.

An East India Company warehouse dating from 1775; now a charming
split-level restaurant with a lovely terrace and harbour views. Seafood
is the strength, with classic Swedish dishes on the 'Wagner' menu and
modern Nordic choices on the 'Trägårdh' menu. At lunch they offer a
buffet and a concise version of the à la carte.

SK MAT & MÄNNISKOR ✿

SWEDISH • BRASSERIE • COSY

Johannebergsgatan 24 ✉ 412 55 **PLAN: C3**
TEL. 031-812 5 80 (booking essential) – **www**.skmat.se
Closed 6 weeks summer, 2 weeks Christmas, Sunday and
bank holidays
Menu 595 SEK – Carte 515/550 SEK (dinner only)

Chef:
Stefan Karlsson

Specialities:
Cured cod with shrimps and
elderflower. Swedish strip-loin
with parsley mayonnaise and fried
bread. Blueberries with lemon curd
and burnt meringue.

The main focal point of this cosy restaurant is the completely open
kitchen; not only can you watch the chefs at work but they also deliver
your food. The effort put into sourcing and the reverence with which
ingredients are treated is commendable and dishes are exciting and
packed with flavour.

THÖRNSTRÖMS KÖK ✿

CLASSIC CUISINE • NEIGHBOURHOOD •
ROMANTIC   XxX 🍴 A/C ⟷

Teknologgatan 3 ✉ 411 32 PLAN: C3
TEL. 031-16 20 66 (booking essential) – **www**.thornstromskok.com
Closed 8 July-15 August, 23 December-5 January, Easter and
Sunday
Menu 465 SEK – Carte 445/760 SEK (dinner only)

Chef:
Håkan Thörnström

Specialities:
Arctic char with mussels and clams.
Sirloin of beef with fermented
onion butter. Sorrel mousse, milk
foam, red berries and vanilla.

An elegant, long-standing restaurant with a stunning wine cave; set
in a quiet residential area and run by a welcoming, knowledgeable
team. There's a good choice of menus, including 3 different tasting
options. Precise, confident, classically based cooking uses top quality
produce to create pronounced flavours.

28+ ✿

MODERN CUISINE • CHIC   XxX 🍴 A/C ⟷

Götabergsgatan 28 ✉ 411 34 PLAN: C3
TEL. 031-20 21 61 – **www**.28plus.se
Closed 4 July-22 August, Christmas-New Year, Sunday, Monday and
bank holidays
Menu 895 SEK – Carte 565/655 SEK (dinner only)

Specialities:
Sweetbreads with ramsons, morels
and cress. Loin of salted cod
with fermented garlic gnocchi.
Liquorice, lemon, condensed milk
and lemon sorbet.

This passionately run basement restaurant has been a Gothenburg
institution for over 30 years. Modern cooking showcases prime
seasonal ingredients, skilfully blending French and Swedish influences
to create intricate, flavourful dishes. There's an exceptional cheese
selection and an outstanding wine list.

UPPER HOUSE ❀

SWEDISH • ELEGANT • CHIC   XxxX 🏵 ⪵ ⚹ AC

Upper House Hotel • Mässans Gata 24, Gothia Towers (25th
Floor) ✉ 402 26 PLAN: D3
TEL. 031-708 82 00 (booking essential) – www.upperhouse.se
Closed 9 July-9 August, 23-25 December, Sunday and Monday
Menu 1250 SEK (dinner only) (tasting menu only)

Specialities:
Quail egg, lemon and dried bleak roe.
Courgette flower with sweetbreads
and tomato. Cinnamon madeleine
with apple butter.

Look out from the 25th floor over 360° of twinkling city lights. Start
with 'nibbles' in the plush bar then watch your bread being cooked
over a hot stone. The set menu offers elaborate, visually pleasing,
flavourful dishes made with an abundance of fresh, local ingredients.
Service is attentive and professional.

FAMILJEN 😊

SCANDINAVIAN • VINTAGE • DESIGN   ✗ 🏵 🏠 AC

Arkivgatan 7 ✉ 411 34 PLAN: C3
TEL. 031-20 79 79 (booking essential) – www.restaurangfamiljen.se
Closed Christmas and Sunday
Menu 355/455 SEK – Carte 335/575 SEK (dinner only)

A lively, friendly eatery divided into three parts: a bar with bench
seating and an open kitchen; a bright red room with a characterful
cellar and a glass wine cave; and a superb wrap-around terrace.
Cooking is good value and portions are generous; there's an appealing
wine, beer and cocktail list too.

SOMM 😊

MODERN CUISINE • FRIENDLY • COSY

Lorensbergsgatan 8 ✉ 411 36 **PLAN: C3**
TEL. 031-28 28 40 – **www**.somm.se
Closed 23-27 December, 1 January and July
Menu 395 SEK – Carte 485/585 SEK (dinner only)

A simply but warmly decorated neighbourhood bistro, with contemporary artwork and a cosy, friendly feel. Quality seasonal ingredients are used to create tasty modern dishes, which feature on an à la carte and various tasting menus. The wine list offers great choice and the service is charming and professional.

LA CUCINA ITALIANA 🍴

ITALIAN • FRIENDLY

Skånegatan 33 ✉ 412 52 **PLAN: C/D3**
TEL. 031-16 63 07 (booking essential) – **www**.lacucinaitaliana.nu
Closed Christmas, Easter, midsummer and Sunday
Menu 400/700 SEK – Carte 475/730 SEK (dinner only)

An intimate and enthusiastically run restaurant consisting of 6 tables. Choose between the à la carte, a 3 course menu and a 6 course surprise tasting 'journey'. The chef-owner regularly travels to Italy to buy cheeses, meats and wines.

DORSIA 🍴

MODERN CUISINE • EXOTIC DÉCOR •
ROMANTIC

XX 器 ♫ A/C ⇔

Dorsia Hotel • Trädgårdsgatan 6 ✉ 411 08 PLAN: B2
TEL. 031-790 10 00 – **www**.dorsia.se

Menu 185/385 SEK – Carte 595/770 SEK

A dramatic hotel dining room split over two levels, with gloriously quirky lighting, striking flower arrangements by the owner and belle époque oil paintings hanging proudly on the walls. Local fish features highly and puddings are worth saving room for. Ask for the rare wine book – you'll be impressed!

FISKEKROGEN 🍴

SEAFOOD • ELEGANT • COSY

XX 器 A/C ⇔

Lilla Torget 1 ✉ 411 18 PLAN: B2
TEL. 031-10 10 05 – **www**.fiskekrogen.com
Closed Christmas-New Year, midsummer, Easter and Sunday

Carte dinner 365/775 SEK (dinner only)

A charming seafood restaurant which is set within a columned 1920s Grand Café and showcases top quality produce. 'Bifångst' is its second smaller dining area which offers a tasting menu of modern small plates.

HOS PELLE ⅈO

TRADITIONAL CUISINE • NEIGHBOURHOOD ⅄

Djupedalsgatan 2 ⊠ 413 07 **PLAN: A3**
TEL. 031-12 10 31 – **www**.hospelle.com
Closed 22-27 December, July, Easter, Saturday lunch and Sunday
Menu 465 SEK – Carte dinner 290/580 SEK

An established neighbourhood eatery located close to the castle;
you can eat in the wine bar or one of two cosy, rustic dining rooms.
Cooking is stout, seasonal and satisfying; the concise set dinner menu
has suggested wine pairings.

KOMETEN ⅈO

SCANDINAVIAN • FAMILY • NEIGHBOURHOOD XX ⛱

Vasagatan 58 ⊠ 411 37 **PLAN: C2**
TEL. 031-13 79 88 (booking essential) – **www**.restaurangkometen.se
Closed midsummer, 23-27 December and 1 January

Carte 435/775 SEK

The oldest restaurant in town has a classic façade and clubby feel;
it opened in 1934 and is now part-owned by celebrated chef Leif
Mannerström. Sweden's culinary traditions are kept alive here in
generous, tasty dishes.

MAGNUS & MAGNUS ⸙⃝

CREATIVE • INTIMATE • NEIGHBOURHOOD

Magasinsgatan 8 ⊠ 411 18 PLAN: B2
TEL. 031-13 30 00 – www.magnusmagnus.se
Closed 24-25 December, Sunday and Monday
Menu 555/795 SEK – Carte 585/605 SEK (dinner only)

A trendy restaurant with a warm, intimate atmosphere, a central bar, an open kitchen and a bright, well-informed team. Modern Nordic cooking has the occasional Asian twist; most diners plump for the set 4 course menu.

SPISA ⸙⃝

MEDITERRANEAN CUISINE • TAPAS BAR

Övre Husargatan 3 ⊠ 411 22 PLAN: B3
TEL. 031-386 06 10 – www.spisamatbar.se
Menu 295/495 SEK – Carte 305/445 SEK (dinner only)

Contemporary restaurant set a short walk from the city centre in an up-and-coming area and frequented by a lively, sociable crowd. The menu offers tasty sharing plates with French, Spanish and Italian origins. Try a cocktail too!

CENTRE

SWEA HOF ⅈO

MODERN CUISINE • CHIC   ✕✕ AC 🚗

Elite Plaza Hotel • Västra Hamngatan 3 ✉ 404 22 PLAN: B2
TEL. 031-720 40 40 – **www**.sweahof.se
Closed 23-27 December
Menu 155/260 SEK – Carte 330/1015 SEK

Striking hotel restaurant in an impressive glass-enclosed
courtyard. Start with drinks in the bar, then head to the spacious
dining room. Fresh, modern cooking combines French and
Scandinavian influences; the lunch menu is concise.

SWEDISH TASTE ⅈO

MODERN CUISINE • FASHIONABLE   ✕✕ ⇔

Sankt Eriksgatan 6 ✉ 411 05 PLAN: B1
TEL. 031-13 27 80 – **www**.swedishtaste.com
Closed 3 July-11 August, Christmas, Saturday lunch and Sunday
Menu 315/535 SEK – Carte 520/835 SEK

A three-storey venture near the Opera House, consisting of a
restaurant, a café, a deli and a cookery school. Lunch is traditional;
more elaborate, contemporary dishes follow at dinner. Produce is top
quality and flavours are authentic.

TOSO ⅋⚬

ASIAN • BISTRO • EXOTIC DÉCOR ✗ A/C

Götaplatsen ⊠ 412 55 PLAN: C3
TEL. 031-787 98 00 – **www**.toso.nu
Closed Christmas and bank holidays
Menu 530 SEK – Carte 360/525 SEK (dinner only)

There's something for everyone at this modern Asian restaurant,
where terracotta warriors stand guard and loud music pumps through
the air. Dishes mix Chinese and Japanese influences; start with some
of the tempting small plates.

TRATTORIA LA STREGA ⅋⚬

ITALIAN • FRIENDLY • BISTRO ✗ ⌂

Aschebergsgatan 23b ⊠ 411 33 PLAN: B3
TEL. 031-18 15 01 (booking essential) – **www**.trattorialastrega.se
Closed July and 24 December-6 January
Menu 500 SEK – Carte 300/520 SEK (dinner only)

A lively little trattoria in a quiet residential area; run by a charming
owner. Sit at a candlelit table to enjoy authentic, boldly flavoured
Italian cooking and well-chosen wines. Signature dishes include pasta
with King crab ragout.

TVÅKANTEN ⅈ◯

TRADITIONAL CUISINE • BRASSERIE

Kungsportsavenyn 27 ⊠ 411 36 PLAN: C3
TEL. 031-18 21 15 – www.tvakanten.se
Closed Christmas, Easter, midsummer and bank holidays
Carte 335/655 SEK

Set in a prime corner position on one of the city's most famous streets.
A busy bar leads to a cosy cellar-style dining room. Classical menus
range from snacks and brunch to a more ambitious à la carte; there's
also a great wine list.

VRÅ ⅈ◯

JAPANESE • BISTRO • SIMPLE

Clarion Hotel Post • Drottningtorget 10 ⊠ 411 03 PLAN: C2
TEL. 031-619 0 60 – www.restaurangvra.se
Closed Sunday, Monday and Friday
Menu 395 SEK – Carte 625/689 SEK (dinner only)

A modern hotel restaurant run by an attentive, knowledgeable team.
Their tagline is 'Swedish ingredients, Japanese flavours' and the
produce is top quality. Choose the 8 course set menu or a menu with
3 core dishes which you can add to.

CLARION H. POST

HISTORIC • BUSINESS • MODERN

Drottningtorget 10 ✉ 411 03 PLAN: C2
TEL. 031-619 00 – **www**.clarionpost.se
500 rm ☕ – 🛇 1490/2090 SEK 🛇🛇 1690/2290 SEK – 3 suites
VRÅ – See restaurant listing

Stunning neoclassical Post Office from the 1920s; now a modern business hotel with extensive conference facilities. Ask for a bedroom in the original building as they have higher ceilings. Relax in the rooftop pool, the impressive spa or the cool ground floor bar. Norda is a slick New York style restaurant; vRÅ offers modern Japanese cuisine.

ELITE PARK AVENUE

BUSINESS • CHAIN • MODERN

Kungsportsavenyn 36-38 ✉ 400 15 PLAN: C3
TEL. 031-727 10 76 – **www**.parkavenuecafe.se
317 rm ☕ – 🛇 1050/2350 SEK 🛇🛇 1250/2750 SEK – 9 suites

Set in a lively location by the Museum of Art, a 1950s building with a stylish interior and spacious, well-equipped bedrooms – the rooftop suites come with balconies. Eat in the English cellar pub; the small Italian eatery-cum-nightclub; or the informal bistro, which mixes French and Swedish cooking.

ELITE PLAZA

LUXURY • MODERN

Västra Hamngatan 3 ✉ 402 22 **PLAN: B2**
TEL. 031-720 40 40 – **www**.elite.se
Closed 23-27 December
127 rm ☲ – ♦ 1700/2700 SEK ♦♦ 2200/4500 SEK – 3 suites
SWEA HOF – See restaurant listing

Elegant former bank dating back to the 19C, featuring a grand staircase, ornate ceilings and a Venetian-style sitting room. The team are welcoming and service is personalised. Bedrooms seamlessly blend the classical and the modern.

UPPER HOUSE

LUXURY • MODERN

Mässans Gata 24, Gothia Towers (25th Floor) ✉ 402 26 **PLAN: D3**
TEL. 031-708 82 00 – **www**.upperhouse.se
53 rm ☲ – ♦ 2890/5390 SEK ♦♦ 2890/5390 SEK – 1 suite

UPPER HOUSE ✿ – See restaurant listing

Set at the top of one of the Gothia Towers; take in the dramatic view from the terrace or from the lovely three-storey spa. Spacious bedrooms are filled with top electronic equipment and Scandic art – the duplex suites are sublime.

AVALON

BUSINESS • MODERN

♞ ♿ ⛵ 🕸 AC 🛎 🚗

Kungstorget 9 ✉ 411 17 PLAN: B2
TEL. 031-751 02 00 – **www**.avalonhotel.se
101 rm ⌂ – ♦ 1245/2445 SEK ♦♦ 1445/2745 SEK – 3 suites

A boutique hotel in a great location near the shops, theatres and harbour. Designer bedrooms have the latest mod cons and come with stylish bathrooms; the penthouse suites have balconies. Relax in the rooftop pool then head for the all-day bistro, which opens onto the piazza and serves international cuisine.

RADISSON BLU RIVERSIDE

BUSINESS • CHAIN • MODERN

⟨ ♞ ♿ 🕸 🛌 AC 🛎 🚗

Lindholmspiren 4, Lindholmen Science Park (West: 4 km by Götaälvbron or take free shuttle ferry from Rosenlund 7am-7pm) ✉ 417 56
TEL. 031-383 40 00 – **www**.radissonblu.se/riversidehotel-gothenburg.com
265 rm ⌂ – ♦ 1200/2400 SEK ♦♦ 1300/2500 SEK – 7 suites

Striking waterfront hotel in the Science Park; a regular shuttle bus operates to the city centre. The rooftop wellness complex has a lovely terrace and hot tub. Some of the modern bedrooms afford great river and city views. The open-plan dining area offers a mix of classical and innovative Swedish cuisine.

SCANDIC RUBINEN

BUSINESS • CHAIN • MODERN

Kungsportsavenyn 24 ✉ 400 14 PLAN: C3
TEL. 031-751 54 00 – www.rubybar.se
289 rm ⌫ – 👤 790/2290 SEK 👥 990/2490 SEK – 3 suites

Set in the heart of town, on the main street, close to the shops and
city sights. Half of the bedrooms are stylish and modern, while the
others have a classic Scandic style. Relax in the spa or out beside
the lovely rooftop bar with some nibbles or cold meats, then dine
overlooking the Avenue.

DORSIA

TOWNHOUSE • FAMILY • ART DÉCO

Trädgårdsgatan 6 ✉ 411 08 PLAN: B2
TEL. 031-790 10 00 – www.dorsia.se
37 rm ⌫ – 👤 1950 SEK 👥 2550/6950 SEK
DORSIA – See restaurant listing

Exuberant, eccentric, seductive and possibly a little decadent, this
townhouse hotel comes with a theatrical belle époque style, where
art from the owner's personal collection, fine fabrics and rich colours
add to the joie de vivre. The restaurant is equally vibrant and the
atmosphere suitably relaxed. The Salon serves small plates from
Friday-Sunday.

EGGERS

TRADITIONAL • CLASSIC

Drottningtorget 2-4 ✉ 411 03 PLAN: B2
TEL. 031-333 44 44 - www.hoteleggers.se
Closed 23-26 December
69 rm ☕ - 🚹 1020/1925 SEK 👫 1340/2490 SEK

Smart 1859 railway hotel that opened with electricity and telephones in every room. The warm, welcoming interior features old wrought iron, stained glass and period furnishings. The characterful restaurant still has its original wallpaper, and offers Swedish classics and international favourites.

NOVOTEL GÖTEBORG

CHAIN • BUSINESS • FUNCTIONAL

Klippan 1 (Southwest: 3.5 km by Andréeg taking Kiel-Klippan Ö exit, or boat from Rosenlund) ✉ 438 33
TEL. 031-720 22 00 - www.novotel.se
151 rm ☕ - 🚹 990/1910 SEK 👫 1090/2010 SEK - 1 suite

Close to the foot ferry, a converted waterfront brewery where you can still buy some vintage Porter beers. The clean, bright interior affords views of the Göta Älv river. Bedrooms are spacious and have a Scandic style; pay the extra for a water view. The restaurant offers Swedish and international classics.

PIGALLE

TOWNHOUSE · FAMILY · CONTEMPORARY

Södra Hamngatan 2A ⊠ 411 06 **PLAN: B2**
TEL. 031-80 29 21 – **www**.hotelpigalle.se
38 rm ⌑ – **♦** 1000/1700 SEK **♦♦** 1700/2600 SEK

A top-hatted manager will welcome you to the reception-cum-welcome-bar of this quirky hotel, which is set within the walls of a historic building. The décor is bold and eclectic, with dramatic features and plenty of personality. In the restaurant you can choose to sit at proper tables or on comfy sofas.

FLORA

FAMILY · FUNCTIONAL

Grönsakstorget 2 ⊠ 411 17 **PLAN: B2**
TEL. 031-13 86 16 – **www**.hotelflora.se
Closed Christmas
65 rm ⌑ – **♦** 860/1960 SEK **♦♦** 1190/2240 SEK

This well-located Victorian mid-terrace is nicely run and has a relaxed, funky feel. Bedrooms benefit from high ceilings; ask for one of the newer, designer rooms. The bar-lounge is a popular spot and doubles as the breakfast room.

RIVER RESTAURANT ON THE PIER ⋔

MODERN CUISINE • FRIENDLY

Dockepiren (West: 6 km by Götaälvbron and Lundbyleden, or boat from Rosenlund) ⊠ 417 64
TEL. 031-510000 (booking advisable) – **www**.riverrestaurant.se
Closed 2 weeks January, Christmas, Saturday lunch, Sunday and Monday

Menu 400/700 SEK – Carte 400/800 SEK

A delightful waterfront restaurant overlooking the city and harbour, with a bright, modern ground floor and an elegant upper level. Come at lunch for an unfussy set menu or at dinner for a seasonal à la carte of hearty Scandic dishes.

VILLAN 🏠

TRADITIONAL • MODERN

Sjöportsgatan 2 (West: 6 km by Götaälvbron and Lundbyleden, or boat from Rosenlund) ⊠ 417 64
TEL. 031-725 77 77 – **www**.hotelvillan.com

26 rm ⌖ – ♦ 1150/1700 SEK ♦♦ 1400/2100 SEK

Characterful wood-clad, family-run house; once home to a shipbuilding manager and later floated over to this location. The stylish interior has smart, clean lines. Contemporary bedrooms boast good mod cons – No.31 has a sauna and a TV in the bathroom. The first floor restaurant overlooks the river.

LANDVETTER AIRPORT HOTEL

BUSINESS • MODERN

会 も 煞 杰 AC 衤 P

Flygets Hotellväg (East: 30 km by Rd 40) ✉ 438 13
TEL. 031-97 75 50 – www.landvetterairporthotel.com
186 rm ☕ – † 1495/1995 SEK †† 1595/2495 SEK – 1 suite

Located just minutes from the airport terminal but in a peaceful
setting; unusually, it's family-run. The light, open interior has a calm
air and a fresh Scandic style; bedrooms are sleek and modern. The
informal restaurant offers a mix of Swedish and global dishes, along
with a BBQ and grill menu at dinner.

MALMÖ
Sweden

Michelin

Malmö was founded in the 13C under Danish rule and it wasn't until 1658 that it entered Swedish possession and subsequently established itself as one of the world's biggest shipyards. The building of the 8km long Oresund Bridge in 2000 reconnected the city with Denmark and a year later, the Turning Torso apartment block was built in the old shipyard district, opening up the city to the waterfront. Once an industrial hub, this 'city of knowledge' has impressively green credentials: buses run on natural gas and there are

400km of bike lanes. There's plenty of green space too; you can picnic in Kungsparken or Slottsparken, sit by the lakes in Pildammsparken or pet the farm animals in 'Folkets'. At the heart of this vibrant city lie three squares: Gustav Adolfs Torg, Stortorget and Lilla Torg, connected by a pedestrianised shopping street. You'll find some of Malmö's oldest buildings in Lilla Torg, along with bustling open-air brasseries; to the west is Scandinavia's oldest surviving Renaissance castle and its beautiful gardens – and beyond that, the 2km Ribersborg Beach with its open-air baths.

North is Gamla Väster with its charming houses and galleries, while south is Davidshall, filled with designer boutiques and chic eateries. Further south is Möllevångstorget, home to a throng of reasonably priced Asian and Middle Eastern shops.

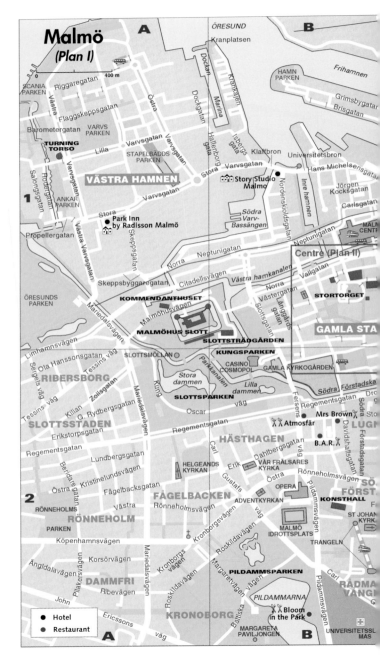

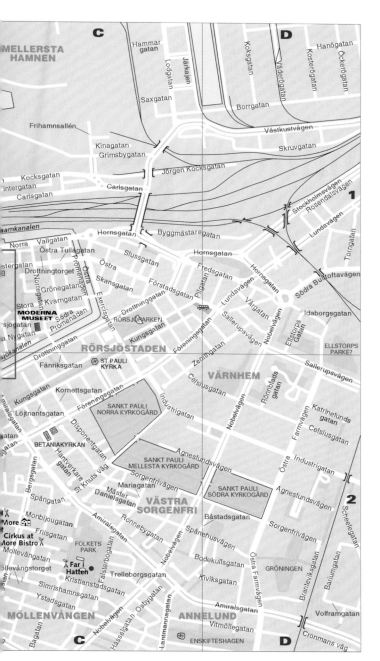

VOLLMERS ✿✿

CENTRE

CREATIVE · ELEGANT · INTIMATE

XX A/C ⟷

Tegelgårdsgatan 5 ✉ 211 33 PLAN: E2
TEL. 040-57 97 50 (booking essential) – **www**.vollmers.nu
Closed 3 weeks July, 1 week January and Sunday
Menu 650/995 SEK (dinner only) (tasting menu only)

Chef:
Mats Vollmer

Specialities:
Cabbage, sherry and lardo. Lamb
with salsify and liquorice. Rhubarb,
lavender and sour cream.

An intimate, elegant restaurant with charming, professional service,
set in a pretty 19C townhouse. Here the talented Mats Vollmer
showcases some of the area's finest seasonal ingredients in set 4, 6
or 8 course menus of intricate and elaborate modern dishes, which
are innovative, perfectly balanced and full of flavour.

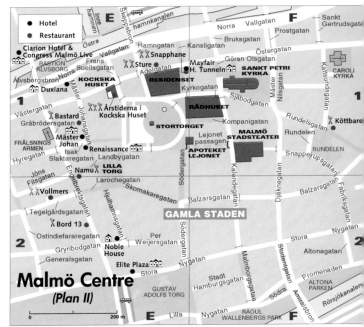

BLOOM IN THE PARK ❀

CREATIVE • DESIGN • CHIC

Pildammsvägen 17 ✉ 214 66 PLAN: B2
TEL. 040-793 63 (booking advisable) – www.bloominthepark.se
Closed 24 December, Easter, Sunday and bank holidays
Menu 695 SEK (dinner only) (surprise menu only)

Chef:
Titti Qvärnström

Specialities:
Weever fish with kohlrabi, lemon
and soya. Goat with beans, black
olives and tomato chutney.
Raspberries with yoghurt and white
chocolate.

A restaurant with a difference: it has no menu and no wine list! Boldly
flavoured, eye-catching dishes use imaginative, original combinations
of top quality ingredients, including organic herbs and flowers from
their greenhouse. It's set in a pretty lakeside lodge and has a stylish
interior and a waterside terrace.

STURE ❀

FRENCH • FRIENDLY • NEIGHBOURHOOD

Adelgatan 13 ✉ 211 22 PLAN: E1
TEL. 040-12 12 53 – www.restaurantsture.com
Closed Christmas and 1 January
Menu 950 SEK (dinner only) (tasting menu only)

Chef:
Karim Khouani

Specialities:
Foie gras with truffle and cotton
candy. Turbot, Oscietra caviar and
oyster cream. Pistachio soufflé
with griottines.

Accomplished chef, Karim Khouani, has brought his exciting blend of
French and Scandic cooking from the country into the centre of the
city, reinvigorating this culinary institution. Top quality ingredients
are used to create inventive, well-balanced and sublimely flavoured
dishes.

BASTARD 😊

MODERN • TRENDY   ✗ 🛜 AC

Mäster Johansgatan 11 ✉ 211 21   PLAN: E1
TEL. 040-12 13 18 (booking advisable) – **www**.bastardrestaurant.se
Closed Christmas, New Year, Easter, midsummer,
Sunday and Monday

Carte 245/355 SEK (dinner only)

Popular with locals, this is a bustling venue with an edgy, urban vibe.
Style-wise, schoolroom meets old-fashioned butcher's, with vintage
wood furniture, tiled walls, moody lighting and an open kitchen. Small
plates offer nose-to-tail eating with bold, earthy flavours; start with
a Bastard Plank to share.

CIRKUS AT MORE BISTRO 😊

MODERN • BISTRO • COLOURFUL   ✗ ♿ 🛜

More Hotel • Norra Skolgatan 24 ✉ 214 22   PLAN: C2
TEL. 040-23 62 50 – **www**.themorebistro.com
Closed Christmas-New Year, Easter, Saturday lunch and dinner
Sunday-Tuesday

Menu 395/595 SEK – Carte 365/550 SEK

It's housed in a former chocolate factory – now a contemporary
aparthotel – and has a name inspired by its resemblance to a 'big top',
with its circular shape and coloured drapes which hang around the
ceiling. Modern dishes with an international edge use regional
ingredients; there's a limited menu at lunch.

NAMU 🐼

KOREAN • FRIENDLY • SIMPLE   ✗ 🏠 A/C

Landbygatan 5 ✉ 21134 PLAN: E1
TEL. 040-12 14 90 – **www**.namu.nu
Closed 24 December, 2-17 January, Sunday and Monday

Carte 275/400 SEK

Mouthwatering, colourful, zingy food from a past Swedish MasterChef
winner blends the authenticity of Korean dishes with a modern
Scandinavian touch – and all at prices that won't break the bank.
Cookbooks line the shelves and friendly service adds to the lively
atmosphere.

ÅRSTIDERNA I KOCKSKA HUSET ⅏

TRADITIONAL • ELEGANT • HISTORIC   ✗✗ 🏠 🖨

Frans Suellsgatan 3 ✉ 211 22 PLAN: E1
TEL. 040-23 09 10 – **www**.arstiderna.se
Closed July, Easter, 24-26 December, Saturday lunch, Sunday and
bank holidays

Menu 435/650 SEK – Carte 515/800 SEK

Set in softly lit, vaulted cellars, this elegant, formal restaurant is a
city institution. Classic cooking proves a match to its surroundings,
with local, seasonal ingredients proudly used to create traditional
Swedish dishes.

ATMOSFÄR ⑩

SWEDISH • NEIGHBOURHOOD

Fersens väg 4 ✉ 211 42 **PLAN: B2**
TEL. 040-12 50 77 – **www**.atmosfar.com
Closed Christmas, Saturday lunch and Sunday
Menu 125/350 SEK – Carte 295/395 SEK

A formal yet relaxed eatery on the main road; dine at the bar, in the restaurant or on the pavement terrace. The menu consists of small plates, of which three or four should suffice. Fresh Skåne cooking is delivered with a light touch.

B.A.R. ⑩

MODERN • WINE BAR • NEIGHBOURHOOD

Erik Dahlbersgatan 3 ✉ 211 48 **PLAN: B2**
TEL. 040-17 01 75 (booking advisable) – **www**.barmalmo.se
Closed Easter, Christmas, Sunday and Monday
Menu 395 SEK – Carte 340/430 SEK (dinner only)

In trendy Davidshall is this lively wine-bar-cum-restaurant named after its owners, Besnick and Robert. The interesting modern menu tends towards the experimental; expect dishes like Jerusalem artichoke ice cream with hazelnut mayo.

BISTRO STELLA ⚬

MODERN • NEIGHBOURHOOD • PUB

Linnégatan 25, Limhamn (Southwest: 7 km by Limhamnsvägen:
bus 4 from Central station) ✉ 216 12
TEL. 040-15 60 40 – **www**.bistrostella.se
Closed midsummer, Christmas, Sunday and Monday

Carte 289/635 SEK (dinner only)

A lively gastropub in a residential area not far from the Oresund
Bridge. Its bright, cosy bar sits between two dining rooms and its
menu features pub dishes like burgers, fish and chips and charcuterie
platters. Cooking is rustic and tasty.

BORD 13 ⚬

CREATIVE • WINE BAR • FRIENDLY

Engelbrektsg 13 ✉ 211 33 **PLAN: E2**
TEL. 042-587 88 – **www**.bord13.se
Closed Christmas, 1 January, Sunday and Monday

Menu 400/700 SEK (dinner only) (tasting menu only)

Sister to B.A.R restaurant, is the bright, spacious and stylish 'Table
13', which offers a set 3 or 6 course menu and a diverse selection
of biodynamic wines. Original Nordic cooking has some interesting
texture and flavour combinations.

FAR I HATTEN 🍴🔘

SWEDISH · RUSTIC · FRIENDLY

Folkets Park ✉ 214 37 **PLAN: C2**
TEL. 040-615 36 51 – **www**.farihatten.se
Closed Christmas
Menu 360/520 SEK (dinner only and lunch June-August)

This unique restaurant is set in a wooden chalet in the lovely Folkets Park and has a cosy, informal feel, with colourful lights and regular live music in the summer. 4 or 6 course menus list well-presented classics with a creative edge.

KÖTTBAREN 🍴🔘

MEATS AND GRILLS · SIMPLE · FRIENDLY

Rundelsgatan ✉ 211 26 **PLAN: F1**
TEL. 040-635 89 01 – **www**.kottbaren.se
Closed 15-16 April, 24-25 December, 1 January, Easter and midsummer
Menu 99/395 SEK – Carte dinner 245/500 SEK

A trendy restaurant with an open kitchen and a relaxed feel, set in the Caroli shopping centre: lunch is a help-yourself buffet, while dinner offers classic Swedish dishes alongside good value, good quality Swedish meats cooked on the grill.

MRS BROWN ⑩

TRADITIONAL • WINE BAR • TRENDY

Storgatan 26 ⊠ 211 42 PLAN: B2
TEL. 040-97 22 50 – **www**.mrsbrown.se
Closed 24 December, Easter, midsummer and Sunday
Menu 395 SEK – Carte 385/490 SEK (dinner only)

This retro brasserie's bar opens at 3pm for drinks and nibbles, while
the kitchen opens at 6pm. Make sure you try one of the cocktails! Well-
presented unfussy cooking has a modern edge and showcases the
region's ingredients.

REBELL ⑩

MODERN • TRENDY • BISTRO

Friisgatan 8B ⊠ 211 46 PLAN: C2
TEL. 040-97 97 35 – **www**.restaurangrebell.se
Closed Christmas, Easter, Saturday lunch and Sunday
Menu 385 SEK (dinner) – Carte 359/450 SEK

An informal, contemporary bistro with a stark, simple feel, serving
vibrant and tasty modern interpretations of local dishes, with ribs
the speciality. A cool soundtrack and locally brewed unfiltered beer
add to the fun.

SNAPPHANE 🍴

MODERN CUISINE • TRENDY • INTIMATE 　 XX AC 🦿

Mayfair Hotel Tunneln • Adelgatan 4 ✉ 211 22 PLAN: E1
TEL. 040-15 01 00 (booking essential) – **www**.snapphane.nu
Closed 22-26 December, 1 January, Easter and Sunday

Menu 225/495 SEK (dinner only)

An elegant, intimate bistro with an open-plan kitchen at its centre.
Innovative modern cooking uses top quality ingredients and dishes
are well-presented, well-balanced and full of flavour. Service is
friendly and professional.

CLARION H. AND CONGRESS MALMÖ LIVE 　

BUSINESS • MODERN • FUNCTIONAL
≪ ⚡ ⛓ 🐾 🛁 AC 🧖 🚗

Dag Hammarskjölds Torg 2 ✉ 211 18 PLAN: E1
TEL. 040-20 75 00 – **www**.choicehotels.com
444 rm ⌂ – 🛏 1080/2480 SEK 🛏🛏 1180/2780 SEK – 2 suites

The city's second tallest building affords a superb 360° view of the
city; choose a bedroom on the upper floors for a view of the Oresund
Bridge and Denmark. Kitchen & Table's eclectic menu combines
American classics and international influences; enjoy a cocktail in
the adjoining Skybar. The ground floor Eatery Social is an informal
Mexican-themed restaurant and bar.

ELITE PLAZA

BUSINESS • CHAIN • MODERN

Gustav Adolfs torg 49 ⊠ 211 39 PLAN: E2
TEL. 040-664 48 71 – **www**.elite.se
116 rm ⌑ – ♦ 977/2450 SEK ♦♦ 1100/2712 SEK – 1 suite

Behind the wonderful period façade is a smart, up-to-date corporate hotel. Modern bedrooms are a good size: the best look onto a pretty square; the quietest overlook the inner courtyard. The British-themed bar has a pleasant pavement terrace.

MÄSTER JOHAN

BUSINESS • MODERN • PERSONALISED

Mäster Johangatan 13 ⊠ 211 21 PLAN: E1
TEL. 040-664 64 00 – **www**.masterjohan.com
68 rm – ♦ 960/2090 SEK ♦♦ 1190/2320 SEK, ⌑ 145 SEK – 10 suites

Centrally located hotel, just off the main square, with a relaxed and peaceful air. Stylish, well-proportioned bedrooms have luxurious touches. Enjoy a locally sourced organic breakfast under the atrium's glass roof.

RENAISSANCE

BUSINESS • CHAIN • MODERN

Mäster Johansgatan 15 ⊠ 211 21 PLAN: E1
TEL. 040-24 85 00 – www.renaissancemalmo.se
128 rm ⊊ – 🛉 895/2395 SEK 🛉🛉 1045/2545 SEK – 1 suite

A smart hotel on the site of the city's original food market: beamed ceilings and iron columns bring character to the modern interior. Bright, well-equipped bedrooms are quiet considering the hotel's location. There's a colourful bar and a simply furnished restaurant; modern dishes are created using local produce.

STORY STUDIO MALMÖ

CHAIN • BUSINESS • PERSONALISED

Tyfongatan 1 ⊠ 211 19 PLAN: B1
TEL. 040-616 52 00 – www.storyhotels.com
Closed 23-25 December
95 rm ⊊ – 🛉 790/2190 SEK 🛉🛉 790/2190 SEK

The modern, well-equipped bedrooms of this hotel are situated on the 10th-14th floors of a 14 storey building next to the old port, and feature large flat screen TVs and floor to ceiling windows. A ground floor eatery offers French cuisine, while the rooftop restaurant serves Asian-influenced dishes accompanied by a beautiful view over the city and harbour.

DUXIANA

TOWNHOUSE · DESIGN · CONTEMPORARY

斧 ♿ [AC]

Mäster Johansgatan 1 ⊠ 211 21 PLAN: E1
TEL. 040-607 70 00 – www.hotellinmalmo.com
22 rm – 🛉 873/2315 SEK 🛉🛉 1130/2315 SEK, ⊋ 70 SEK

A well-located boutique hotel; owned by the Dux bed company, who
unusually use part of the lobby to showcase their products! Chic,
contemporary bedrooms range from compact singles to elegant junior
suites with a bath in the room. Staff are friendly and professional.
Modern Swedish dishes are served at lunch.

MAYFAIR H. TUNNELN

TOWNHOUSE · HISTORIC · PERSONALISED

斧 🛁

Adelgatan 4 ⊠ 211 22 PLAN: E1
TEL. 040-10 16 20 – www.mayfairhotel.se
81 rm ⊋ – 🛉 800/1300 SEK 🛉🛉 850/2800 SEK
SNAPPHANE – See restaurant listing

An imposing early 17C property steeped in history, with cellars dating
back to 1307; enjoy a complimentary coffee in the classical lounge.
Bedrooms are spotless and homely; some have a spa bath. Snapphane
showcases the latest local, organic ingredients while Malmö Rökeri
specialises in smoked produce: both restaurants are overseen by the
Vollmer brothers.

MORE

TOWNHOUSE • BUSINESS • MODERN

Norra Skolgatan 24 ⊠ 214 22 **PLAN: C2**
TEL. 040-655 10 00 – **www**.themorehotel.com
68 rm ⌧ – **♦** 785/1785 SEK **♦♦** 985/2785 SEK

CIRKUS AT MORE BISTRO 🍴 – See restaurant listing

A striking aparthotel converted from a late 19C chocolate factory. The studios are modern and extremely spacious, with kitchenettes, sofa beds and light loft-style living areas. They are let on a nightly basis but are ideal for longer stays.

PARK INN BY RADISSON MALMÖ

CHAIN • FUNCTIONAL • MODERN

Sjömansgatan 2 ⊠ 211 19 **PLAN: A1**
TEL. 040-628 60 00 – **www**.parkinn.com/hotel-malmo
231 rm ⌧ – **♦** 795/1395 SEK **♦♦** 795/1395 SEK

A good value hotel, well-situated on the Western Harbour beside the World Trade Centre and the Västra Hamnen waterfront. Bedrooms are spacious and well-equipped; the business rooms on the higher floors come with robes and have better views. The Bar & Grill offers easy dining.

NOBLE HOUSE

BUSINESS • FAMILY • FUNCTIONAL

Per Weijersgatan 6 ✉ 21134 PLAN: E2
TEL. 040-664 30 00 - **www**.hotelnoblehouse.se
137 rm - 795/1550 SEK 895/1750 SEK - 2 suites

A centrally located hotel, close to the bus station. Classically furnished, well-equipped bedrooms offer good value for money; ask for a room on one of the upper floors. There's a cosy lounge and a modern restaurant which serves traditional Swedish dishes.

KRAKAS KROG

CREATIVE • RUSTIC • COSY

Kräklings 223, Katthammarsvik
(Southeast: 39 km by 143 on 146) ✉ 623 70
TEL. 0498-530 62 (booking essential) - **www**.krakas.se
Closed October-mid June and Monday-Wednesday
Menu 850/1050 SEK (dinner only and Saturday lunch)

An appealing countryside restaurant with a veranda overlooking the garden and a relaxed, homely ambience; its charming owner boasts an impressive knowledge of wine. Creative cooking utilises the best of Gotland's seasonal ingredients; flavours are intense and combinations stimulating and well-judged. Simple, stylish bedrooms complete the picture.

CENTRE

GOTLAND

FÄVIKEN MAGASINET ❀❀

CREATIVE • INTIMATE • RUSTIC   XxX 🍴 🌙 P

Fäviken 216 ✉ 83005
TEL. 0647-40177 (booking essential) – www.favikenmagasinet.se
Closed 2 weeks Christmas-New Year

Menu 3000 SEK (dinner only) (surprise menu only)

Chef:
Magnus Nilsson

Specialities:
King crab and almost burnt butter.
Boiled trout, bog butter and lichen
porridge. Brown cheese pie.

A unique dining experience in the idyllic setting of a remote hunting
estate. The young, forward-thinking team hunt, forage and preserve
the bounteous crop delivered by the surrounding land. Enthralling,
adventurous cooking is rooted in Scandic tradition; dinner is for a
max. of 16. Bedrooms are cabin style. Enjoy complimentary drinks in
the sauna and tremendous breakfasts.

HOTELL BORGHOLM ❀

MODERN • CLASSIC DÉCOR • FRIENDLY   XX 🦞 ♿ AC

Trädgårdsgatan 15-17, Borgholm (North: 34 km by 136) ✉ 387 31
TEL. 0485-77060 (booking essential) – www.hotellborgholm.com
Closed 1 January-10 March, Monday except June-August and
Sunday

Menu 695/1195 SEK (dinner only and lunch Wednesday-Friday in
winter) (tasting menu only)

Chef:
Karin Fransson

Specialities:
Langoustine with summer cabbage
and smoked marrow. Saddle of
lamb with celery and rosemary
caramel. Quark, raspberry and
white chocolate.

A bright, spacious hotel restaurant hung with vibrant art. The self-
taught chef offers a set 7 course menu based around superlative island
ingredients. Classically based cooking is technically accomplished,
artistically presented and demonstrates a mature understanding of
balance and flavour.

HOTELL BORGHOLM

BUSINESS • CONTEMPORARY • PERSONALISED

🏠

⛷ AC ♿

Trädgårdsgatan 15-17, Borgholm (North: 34 km by 136) ✉ 387 31
TEL. 0485-770 60 – **www**.hotellborgholm.com
Closed 1 January-10 March

41 rm ☕ – 🛏 1400 SEK 🛏🛏 1620/2370 SEK

HOTELL BORGHOLM ❀ – See restaurant listing

A long-standing, personally run and busy hotel in a pretty town; it's
light and bright, with modern art on the walls. Compact, up-to-date
bedrooms have wooden floors and modern furniture. The buffet
breakfasts are comprehensive.

DANIEL BERLIN ❀

CREATIVE • FRIENDLY • SIMPLE

XX 🍴 🛋 P

Diligensvägen 21 ✉ 273 92
TEL. 0417-203 00 (booking essential) – **www**.danielberlin.se
Closed midsummer, 24-30 July, 28 August-3 September, 20-26
November, 18 December-31 January, Tuesday dinner and Thursday
lunch except July-August, Sunday and Monday

Menu 850/1650 SEK (surprise menu only)

Chef:
Daniel Berlin

Specialities:
Seaweed juice with kohlrabi, dill
and horseradish. Lamb with garden
peas and flowers. Honey, goats'
milk and rosemary.

A delightful 150 year old house with a simple, rustic style is home to
this charming family-run restaurant which serves just 5 tables. Dinner
is a feast for the senses, with a surprise menu of 20+ stimulating
modern dishes. Each is made up of a few beautifully fresh, natural
ingredients; many from their own 3 acre garden and the surrounding
countryside.

PM & VÄNNER ⭐

CREATIVE • ELEGANT • INTIMATE   ✗✗✗ 🍴 ⭐ ♿ AC 🔌

PM & Vänner Hotel • Storgatan 22-24 ✉ 352 31
TEL. 0470-75 97 10 (booking essential) – www.pmhotel.se
Closed mid-June to mid-August, 24-31 December and Sunday-Tuesday
Menu 795/1295 SEK (dinner only) (tasting menu only)

Specialities:
Pike-perch with wild asparagus, cicely and apple. Lamb with carrots and preserved plums. Rhubarb with sour cream and almonds.

A formal hotel restaurant serving a set 5 or 10 course menu of sophisticated and original modern Nordic dishes. Their philosophy is based on 'forest, lake and meadow', and most of the ingredients come from surrounding Småland. An extraordinary wine list offers a huge array of vintages from top producers.

PM & VÄNNER 🏘️

BUSINESS • LUXURY • DESIGN
🏋️ ♿ 🧖 🛏️ AC 💆 🚗

Västergaten 10 ✉ 352 31
TEL. 0470-75 97 00 – www.pmhotel.se
74 rm ⬜ – 🛏️ 1290/1950 SEK 🛏️🛏️ 1590/2290 SEK – 1 suite

PM & VÄNNER ⭐ – See restaurant listing

A well-run, very stylish hotel with up-to-date facilities, including an appealing roof terrace with a bar and lounge, a hot tub and a plunge pool, and a bakery, florist and spa. Spacious, stark white bedrooms come with ultra-comfy beds and bespoke toiletries. The buzzy Bistro has a large terrace.

NOTES

MICHELIN IS CONTINUALLY INNOVATING FOR SAFER, CLEANER, MORE ECONOMICAL, BETTER CONNECTED... ALL-ROUND MOBILITY.

Tyres wear more quickly on short urban journeys. ?

TRUE!

You tend to accelerate and brake more often when driving around town so your tyres work harder!
If you are stuck in traffic, keep calm and drive slowly.

Tyre pressure only affects your car's safety. ?

FALSE!

Driving with underinflated tyres (0.5 bar below recommended pressure) doesn't just impact handling and fuel consumption, it will shave 8,000 km off tyre lifespan.
Make sure you check tyre pressure about once a month and before you go on holiday or a long journey.

Fitting **2 winter tyres** on my car guarantees maximum safety.

?

FALSE!

In the winter, especially when temperatures drop below 7°C, to ensure better road holding, all four tyres should be identical and fitted at the same time.

2 WINTER TYRES ONLY = risk of compromised road holding.

4 WINTER TYRES = **safer handling** when cornering, driving downhill and braking.

If you regularly encounter rain, snow or black ice, choose a **MICHELIN Alpin tyre**. This range offers you sharp handling plus a comfortable ride to safely face the challenge of winter driving.

MICHELIN

MICHELIN IS COMMITTED

▶ MICHELIN IS **GLOBAL LEADER IN FUEL-EFFICIENT TYRES** *FOR LIGHT VEHICLES.*

▶ **TO EDUCATE YOUNGSTERS IN ROAD SAFETY,** *INCLUDING CYCLING, MICHELIN ROAD SAFETY CAMPAIGNS WERE RUN IN* **16 COUNTRIES** *IN 2015.*

QUIZ

1 TYRES ARE BLACK SO WHY IS THE MICHELIN MAN WHITE?

Back in 1898 when the Michelin Man was first created from a stack of tyres, they were made of natural rubber, cotton and sulphur and were therefore light-coloured. The composition of tyres did not change until after the First World War when carbon black was introduced. But the Michelin Man kept his colour!

2 HOW LONG HAS MICHELIN BEEN GUIDING TRAVELLERS?

Since 1900. When the MICHELIN guide was first published at the turn of the century, it was claimed that it would last for a hundred years. It's still around today, with new editions published every year, along with online restaurant listings.

3 WHEN WAS THE "BIB GOURMAND" INTRODUCED IN THE MICHELIN GUIDE?

The symbol was created in 1997 but as early as 1954 the MICHELIN guide was recommending "good food at moderate prices". Today, it also features on the ViaMichelin website and on the Michelin Restaurants app.

If you want to enjoy a fun day out and find out more about Michelin, why not visit the l'Aventure Michelin museum and shop in Clermont-Ferrand, France:
www.laventuremichelin.com

A better way forward

INDEX OF...
RESTAURANTS ▯◎

INDEX OF...
HOTELS

CREDITS

101: Michelin ▪ 108: Michelin ▪ 28+: 28+ ▪ 56°: Spisehuset 56° ▪ Aamanns Etablissement: Aamanns Etablissement / Columbus Leth/Aamanns Etablissement ▪ Aarhus Guldsmeden: Guldsmeden ▪ Absalon: Absalon ▪ Adam/Albin by Adam & Albin: Adam/Albin by Adam & Albin ▪ Admiral: Admiral Hotel ▪ AG: AG ▪ Albert: Aki Ras/ Akifoto ltd/Albert / Lauri Mannermaa/Albert ▪ Alberto K: Per Anders Jörgensen/ Alberto K / David Bicho/Alberto K ▪ Alchemist: Alchemist ▪ Alda: Michelin ▪ Alex Sushi: Alex Sushi ▪ Alex Sushi Tjuvholmen: Marius Fiskum/Alex Sushi Tjuvholmen ▪ Alexandra: Alexandra Hotel ▪ Amalie: Michelin ▪ Amass: Amass ▪ Anarki: Michelin ▪ Andersen: Andersen ▪ Arakataka: Michelin ▪ Ärstiderna i Kockska Huset: Ärstiderna i Kockska Huset ▪ Ask: Ask ▪ Ateljé Finne: Ateljé Finne / Aino Huovio/Ateljé Finne ▪ Atmosfär: Atmosfär ▪ Avalon: Avalon ▪ Avenue: Hotel Avenue ▪ A|O|C: Signe Birck/ A|O|C ▪ B.A.R.: B.A.R. / Morgan Ekner/B.A.R. ▪ BA53: Michelin ▪ Babette: Michelin ▪ Bastard: Bastard ▪ Bekkjarvik Gjestgiveri: Bekkjarvik Gjestgiveri / Michelin ▪ Berns: Barabild/Berns / J Strong Design/Berns ▪ Berns Asiatiska: Berns Asiatiska ▪ Bhoga: Bhoga ▪ Bistro Stella: Bistro Stella ▪ Bloom in the Park: Bloom in the Park ▪ Bobergs: Michelin / Bobergs ▪ Bockbakka: Michelin ▪ Bockholmen: Bockholmen ▪ Boqueria: Niklas Nyman/Boqueria / Boqueria ▪ Bord 13: Michelin ▪ Borg: Michelin ▪ Boulevard Social: Boulevard Social / Tuuka Koski/Boulevard Social ▪ Brasserie Belli: Belli ▪ Brasserie Blanche: Michelin ▪ Brasserie Bobonne: Brasserie Bobonne ▪ Brasserie France: Brasserie France / Jimmy Linus/Brasserie France ▪ Brasserie Hansken: Brasserie Hansken ▪ Brasserie Paleo: Michelin ▪ Bronda: Bronda ▪ Bror: Bror ▪ Bryghuset Vendia - Gourmet: Michelin ▪ Canopy by Hilton: Michelin ▪ Carne Famo: Carne Famo ▪ Carousel: Carousel / Michelin ▪ Castenskiold: Castenskiold ▪ Chef & Sommelier: Chef & Sommelier ▪ Ché Fè: Ché Fè ▪ Cirkus at More Bistro: Steffan Anderson/Cirkus at More Bistro ▪ City: Hotel City ▪ Clarion Collection H. Bastion: Clarion Collection H. Bastion ▪ Clarion Collection H. Gabelshus: Clarion Collection H. Gabelshus ▪ Clarion Collection H. Savoy: CF-Wesenberg/Clarion Collection H. Savoy ▪ Clarion Collection H. Wellington: Clarion Collection H. Wellington ▪ Clarion H. & Congress Malmö Live: Clarion H. & Congress Malmö Live ▪ Clarion H. Post: Clarion Hotel Post / Louise Billgert/Clarion Hotel Post ▪ Clarion H.Arlanda Airport: Nordic Choice Hospitality Group AS/Clarion H.Arlanda Airport ▪ Clarion Oslo Airport: Margrethe Myhrer/Nordic Choice Hospitality Group/Clarion Oslo Airport ▪ Clou: Clou ▪ Comfort H. Grand Central: Comfort H. Grand Central ▪ Comwell Aarhus: Comwell ▪ Continental: Continental ▪ Copenhagen Marriott: Copenhagen Marriott ▪ Credo: Michelin ▪ Crowne Plaza Helsinki: Crowne Plaza Helsinki ▪ Cru: Cru / Michelin ▪ D'Angleterre: Hotel d'Angleterre ▪ Daniel Berlin: Michelin ▪ De Fem Stuer: Holmenkollen Park H. Rica ▪ Demo: Juha-Pekka Laakio Oy/Demo ▪ Den Gule Cottage: Anders Schønnemann/Den Gule Cottage ▪ Den Gyldene Freden: Den Gyldene Freden / Jann Lipka/Den Gyldene Freden ▪ Den Røde Cottage: Anders Schønnemann/Den Røde Cottage ▪ Dill: Michelin ▪ Dinner: www. stianbroch.com/Dinner ▪ Diplomat: Louise Billgert/Diplomat / Lindman Photography AB/Diplomat ▪ Djuret: linus hallgren/Djuret ▪ Domestic: Michelin ▪ Dorsia: Dejan Sokolovski/Dorsia ▪ Dorsia (restaurant): Dorsia Restaurant ▪ Dragsholm Slot: Michelin ▪ Duxiana: Duxiana ▪ EAT: Magnus Skoglöf/EAT ▪ Eggers: Hotel Eggers ▪ Ekeberg: Ekeberg ▪ Ekstedt: Per-Anders Jorgensen/Ekstedt ▪ Elite Eden Park: Sandra Birgersdotter/Fotograf Birgersdotter AB/Elite Eden Park ▪ Elite H. Stockholm Plaza: Sandra Birgersdotter/Elite H. Stockholm Plaza / Linda Brostrom/Elite H. Stockholm Plaza ▪ Elite Park Avenue: Fotograf Birgersdotter AB/Elite Park Avenue / Linda Brostrom/Elite Park Avenue ▪ Elite Plaza: Fotograf Birgersdotter AB/Elite Plaza / Linda Brostrom/Elite Plaza ▪ Emo: Emo ▪ Enomania: Enomania ▪ Era Ora: Michelin ▪ Eriks Bakficka: Sören Andersson/Eriks Bakficka ▪ Esperanto: Esperanto ▪ Ett Hem: Ett Hem ▪ Fabian: Fabian ▪ Falsled Kro: Falsled Kro / Michelin ▪ Familjen: Åke E:son Lindman/Familjen / Familjen ▪ Famo: Famo ▪ Famo Metro: Famo Metro ▪ Far I Hatten: Michelin ▪ Farang: Tuuka Koski/Farang ▪ Fäviken Magisinet: Midelia ▪ Feinschmecker: Glenn Karlsrud/Feinschmecker ▪ Ferdinand: Ferdinand ▪ Festningen: Michelin ▪ First H. Atlantic: First H. Atlantic / Jesper Rais/First H. Atlantic ▪ Fiskekrogen: Fiskekrogen ▪ Fjord: Fjord / Werner Anderson/Fjord ▪ Fjäderholmarnas Krog: Fjäderholmarnas Krog ▪ Flora: Lelle Anderzén/Flora / Flora ▪ Formel B: Formel B ▪ Frederiks Have: Frederiks Have ▪ Frederiksgade 42: Lucas Adler Hyldebrandt/Frederiksgade 43 / Lucas Adler Hyldebrandt/Frederiksgade 43 ▪ Frederikshøj: Jesper Rais/Restaurant Frederikshø ▪ Frederiksminde: Michelin ▪ Fru K: Marte Garmann/Nord Magazin/Fru K at Thief Hotel / Marte Garmann/Oat/Fru K at Thief Hotel ▪ Fru Larsen: Fru Larsen / Michelin ▪ Frøken Koch: Frøken Koch ▪ Fäviken Magasinet: Michelin ▪ Gaijin: Tuuka Koski/Gaijin / Gaijin ▪ Gallery: Michelin ▪ Gamle Raadhus: Annette Larsen/Gamle Raadhus ▪ Gammel Mønt: Gammel Mønt / Michelin ▪ Gäst: The Mayor ▪ Gastrologik: Gastrologik ▪ Gastromé: Gastromé ▪ Geist: Restaurant Geist ▪ Geranium: Claes Bech-Poulsen/ Geranium ▪ GLO Hotel Art: GLO Hotel Art / Markus Henttonen/GLO Hotel Art ▪ GLO Hotel Kluuvi: GLO Hotel Kluuvi / Markus Henttonen/GLO Hotel Kluuvi ▪ Godt: Godt ▪ Gorilla: Michelin ▪ Grand: Glenn Roekeberg/Grand Hotel, Oslo / Grand Hôtel / Grand Hôtel, Oslo ▪ Grand Central by Scandic: Scandic Grand Central ▪ Grefsenkollen:

Grefsenkollen ■ Grilliö: Michelin ■ Gro: Gro ■ Grotesk: Grotesk ■ Happolati: Michelin ■ Haven: Hôtel Haven ■ Haymarket by Scandic: Haymarket by Scandic ■ Hebron: Jon Norddahl/Hebron ■ Henne Kirkeby Kro: Henne Kirkeby Kro ■ Hillenberg: Hillenberg ■ Hilton Copenhagen Airport: Hilton Copenhagen Airport ■ Hilton Helsinki Airport: Hilton Helsinki Airport ■ Hilton Helsinki Strand: Hilton Helsinki Strand ■ Holiday Inn Helsinki West Ruoholahti: Michael Schultes/Holiday Inn Helsinki West Ruoholahti ■ Holmenkollen Park H. Rica: Holmenkollen Park H. Rica ■ Holt: Michelin ■ Hos Pelle: Hos Pelle ■ Hos Thea: Hos Thea ■ Hotel Frederiksminde: Hotel Frederiksminde ■ Hotel J: Hotel J ■ Hotel Ritz Aarhus City: Martin Schubert/Hotel Ritz ■ Hotel Royal: Royal H ■ Hotell Borgholm: Hotel Borgholm /Michelin ■ Hummer: Michelin ■ Häktet: Michelin ■ Hærværk: Hærværk ■ Höst: Höst ■ F-Høj: Høj / Jesper Rais/Høj ■ Ibsens: Ibsens Hotel ■ Il Grappolo Blu: Michelin / Il Grappolo Blu ■ Imouto: Imouto ■ Imperial: Imperial ■ Island: Island ■ Juuri: H. Finer/Juuri ■ Kadeau: Marie Louise Munkegaard/Kadeau ■ Kanalen: Harry Nielsen/Kanalen / Kanalen ■ Kaskis: Michelin ■ Katajanokka: Katajanokka /KIMMOLEVONEN/Katajanokka ■ Kiin Kiin: Kiin Kiin ■ Klaus K: Klaus K ■ Koefoed: Koefoed ■ Koka: Maria Bangata/Koka ■ Kokkeriet: Mikkel Adsbøl/Kokkeriet ■ KOKS: Michelin ■ Kometen: Kometen ■ Kong Arthur: Kong Arthur ■ Kong Hans Kaelder: Michelin ■ Kontrast: Michelin ■ Krakas Krog: Michelin ■ Kungsträdgården: Michelin ■ Kurhotel Skodsborg: Michelin ■ Kuurna: Aino Huovio/Kuurna / Kuurna ■ Kähler Spisesalon: Kähler Spisesalon ■ Kämp: Kämp ■ Köttbaren: Köttbaren ■ Kødbyens Fiskebar: Thomas Ibsen/Kødbyens Fiskebar / Mikkel Eis Andersen/Kødbyens Fiskebar ■ L' Enoteca di Mr. Brunello: Michelin / Flavio Clemente ■ L'Altro: L'Altro ■ L'Osteria del Grappolo Blu: Anders Hviid/L'Osteria del Grappolo Blu / L'Osteria del Grappolo Blu ■ La Cucina Italiana: La Cucina Italiana ■ Landvetter Airport Hotel: Erik Nissen Johansen/Landvetter Airport Hotel / Jesper Orrbeck Photography/Landvetter Airport Hotel ■ Lassens: Michelin ■ Le Sommelier: Le Sommelier ■ Lilla Ego: Lilla Ego ■ Lilla Roberts: Michelin / Lilla Roberts ■ Lisa Elmqvist: Michelin / Lisa Elmqvist ■ Lofoten Fiskerestaurant: Lofoten Fiskerestaurant ■ Lumskebugten: Lumskebugten ■ Lux Dag för Dag: Morgan Ekner/Lux Dag för Dag ■ Luzette: Michelin ■ Lydmar: Lydmar / Raphael Cameron/Lydmar ■ Lyon: Lyon / Marco Väkelä/Lyon ■ Lysverket: Michelin ■ Maaemo: Jimmy Linus/Maaemo ■ Magnus & Magnus: Magnus & Magnus ■ Marchal: Michelin ■ Mares: Mares ■ Marv & Ben: Marv & Ben ■ Mash: Lassen's /MASH ■ Mathias Dahlgren-Matbaren: Magnus Skoglöf/ Mathias Dahlgren-Matbaren ■ Matur og Drykkur: Michelin ■ Mayfair H. Tunneln: Mayfair H. Tunneln ■ Mielcke & Hurtigkarl: Alastair Philip Wiper/Mielcke & Hurtigkarl / Jakob Mielcke/Kim Agersten/Mielcke & Hurtigkarl ■ Miss Clara by Nobis: Felix Odell/Miss Clara Hotel ■ Molskroen: Michelin ■ More: More Hotel ■ Mrs Brown: Mrs Brown ■ Muru: Tuukka Koski/Muru ■ Mäster Johan: Mäster Johan ■ Mêlée: Stine Christiansen/Mêlée ■ Møf: Møf ■ Namu: Michelin ■ Niklas: Mathias Nordgren/Niklas / Niklas ■ Nimb: Nimb ■ No.2: No.2 / Signe Roderik/No.2 ■ Nobis: Nobis Hôtel / Louise Billgert/Nobis Hôtel ■ Noble House: Michelin ■ Nodee Barcode: Michelin ■ Nokka: Nokka ■ Nook: Michelin ■ Nordisk Spisehus: Nordisk Spisehus ■ Nosh and Chow: Nosh and Chow ■ Novotel Göteborg: Martin von Brömssen/Novotel Göteborg ■ Oasia: Martin Gravgaard/ Oasia ■ Oaxen Krog: Oaxen Krog ■ Oaxen Slip: magnus/Oaxen Slip / erik olsson photography/Oaxen Slip ■ Ol & Brod: Camilla Stephan/Ol & Brod / Ol & Brod ■ Olo: Michelin ■ Omakase Köttslöjd: Omakase Köttslöjd / Michelin ■ Opera: Marte Eyde Kjuus/Opera / BŒrd Gudim - Oslo - Norway/Opera ■ Operakällaren: Operakällaren ■ Palægade: Michelin ■ Park Inn: Park Inn ■ Park Inn by Radisson: Park Inn by Radisson ■ Pasfall: Michelin ■ Passio: Michelin ■ Pastis: Pastis ■ Paustian: photo by Paustian ■ Pigalle: Pigalle ■ Plah: Plah ■ Pluto: Pluto ■ PM & Vänner: Michelin /PM & Vänner ■ Pocket: Michelin ■ Pondus: Pondus ■ Pony: Marie Louise Munkegaard/Pony / Mikkel Jul Hvilsh/Pony ■ Pop House: Pop House / Jason Strong Photography/Pop House ■ Proviant Östermalm: Proviant ■ Pubologi: Toby Maudsley/Pubologi / Pubologi ■ Radio: Radio ■ Radisson Blu Plaza: Radisson Blu Plaza / Aki Rask/Akifoto ltd/Radisson Blu Plaza / Soeren Dam Thomsen/Radisson Blu Plaza ■ Radisson Blu Riverside: Radisson Blu Riverside ■ Radisson Blu Royal: Radisson Blu Royal / Per Anders Jörgensen/Radisson Blu Royal ■ Radisson Blu Scandinavia: Radisson Blu Scandinavia ■ Radisson Blu Sky City: Pierre Wester AB/Radisson Blu Sky City ■ Radisson Blu Strand: Radisson Blu Strand / Pål Allan/Radisson Blu Strand ■ Ragu: Ragu ■ RE-NAA: Michelin ■ Rebel: Rebel ■ Rebell: Rebell ■ Regina: Michelin ■ Relæ: Per Anders Jörgensen/Relæ ■ Renaissance: Renaissance / Mads Damgaard/Renaissance ■ Restaurant ET: christian b/2010/Restaurant ET / Søren Gammelmark/Restaurant ET ■ Restaurant J: Restaurant J / Per Erik Berglund/Restaurant J ■ restauranteik: Werner Anderson_200/restauranteik / restauranteik ■ Restaurationen: Marie Louise Munkegaard/Restaurationen ■ Retour Steak: Retour Steak ■ Riddargatan: Hôtel Riddargatan ■ Rival: Milla Sterner 2009/ Rival / Rival ■ River Restaurant On The Pier: River Café ■ Rivoli Jardin: Rivoli Jardin / Panu Rissane /Loma Graphics Oy 2008/Rivoli Jardin ■ Rolfs Kök: Rolfs Kök ■ Rosenkrantz: Rosenkrantz ■ Ruths: Ruths ■ Ruths Gourmet Restaurant: Michelin ■ Sabi Omakase: Michelin ■ Saga H. Oslo: Saga H. Oslo ■ Salt: Salt ■ Salutorget: Salutorget ■ Sankt Annae: Restaurant Sankt Annae ■ Savoy: Savoy ■ Scandic Aarhus City: Scandic Aarhus City ■ Scandic Gamla Stan: Michelin / Scandic Gamla Stan ■ Scandic Rubinen: Scandic Rubinen ■ Scandic Vulkan: Scandic Vulkan ■ Sheraton: Sheraton ■ Shibumi: Bohman & Sjöstrand AB/Shibumi ■ Sjömagasinet: Sjömagasinet ■ SK Mat & Människor: SK Mat & Människor ■ Skeppsholmen: Skeppsholmen / Max Plunger 2008/Skeppsholmen ■ Skt. Annæ: Skt. Annæ ■ Sletten: Michelin ■ Slinger Bistro: Slinger Bistro ■ Slotskælderen hos Gitte Kik: Slotskælderen hos Gitte Kik ■ Slotsskøkkenet: Michelin ■ Smak: Åke E:son Lindman/Smak / Smak ■ Smalhans: Niklas Lello/Smalhans / Smalhans ■ Snapphane: Michelin ■ Søllerød Kro: Søllerød Kro ■ Somm: Somm ■ Speceriet: Speceriet ■ Spectrum: Bård Gudim/Spectrum ■ Spis: Spis ■ Spisa: Spisa ■ Stallmästaregården: Max Plunger 2008/Stallmästaregården / Stallmästaregården ■ Stammershalle Badehotel: Michelin ■ Standard - Almanak:

Sarah Coghill/The copenhagenmediacenter.com ▪ Statholderens Mat og Vin Kjeller:
Statholderens Mat og Vin Kjeller ▪ Statholdergaarden: Statholdergaarden ▪ Story
Hotel - Studio Malmo: Michelin ▪ Strand: Strand ▪ Strandvägen 1: Michelin ▪ Studio
at The Standard: Sarah Coghill/The copenhagenmediacenter.com ▪ Sture: Sture ▪
Sturehof: Sturehof ▪ Substans: Søren Gammelmark/Substans ▪ Sushi Sho: Michelin
▪ Svartengrens: Svartengrens / Paul Lindqvist/Svartengrens ▪ Swea Hof: Swea Hof
/ Linda Brostrom/Swea Hof ▪ Swedish Taste: Swedish Taste ▪ Sårt: Sårt ▪ Søllerød
Kro: Søllerød Kro ▪ Taller: Taller ▪ Tango Bar & Kjøkken: Michelin ▪ The Flying Elk:
The Flying Elk / Michelin ▪ The Mayor: The Mayor ▪ The Restaurant by Kroun: Michelin
▪ Theatercaféen: Theatercaféen ▪ Thief: Marcel Lelienhof/Thief / Jim Hensley/Thief
▪ Thörnströms Kök: Thörnströms Kök ▪ Ti Trin Ned: Michelin ▪ Time: Time ▪
Tjuvholmen Sjømagasin: Tjuvholmen Sjømagasin ▪ Toca: Toca ▪ Torni: Torni ▪ Toso:
Toso ▪ Trattoria La Strega: Trattoria La Strega ▪ Tree Top: Michelin ▪ Tvåkanten:
Bengt Samuelsson/Tvåkanten / Tvåkanten ▪ Uformel: Uformel ▪ Ulla Winbladh: Ulla
Winbladh ▪ Ulriksdals Wärdshus: Ulriksdals Wärdshus ▪ Umami: Umami / Dyrløv
Fotografi/Umami ▪ Upper House: Upper House ▪ Vaaghals: Vaaghals / Michelin ▪
Vassa Eggen: Vassa Eggen ▪ Vika Atrium: bedrift/Vika Atrium ▪ Villa Källhagen: Villa
Källhagen ▪ Villa Provence: Villa Provence ▪ Villan: Villan ▪ Vollmers: Michelin ▪
Volt: Morgan Ekner/Volt ▪ VOX: Michelin ▪ VrÅ: Dino/VrÅ ▪ Wedholms Fisk:
Wedholms Fisk ▪ Woodstockholm: Michelin ▪ Yume: Yume ▪ Zink Grill: Zink Grill
▪ Årstiderna i Kockska Huset: Årstiderna i Kockska Huset

Michelin Travel Partner
Société par actions simplifiées au capital de 11 288 880 EUR
27 Cours de l'Île Seguin - 92100 Boulogne-Billancourt (France)
R.C.S. Nanterre 433 677 721
© Michelin 2014
Dépôt légal : février 2017

Printed in Belgium
Typesetting: Nord Compo
Printing-binding: Geers Offset (Gent)